TEACHER'S RESOURCE MASTERS

BLACKLINE MASTERS AND TEACHER'S MANUAL

GRADE 3

SERIES AUTHORS

Judy Bond	Michael Jothen
René Boyer	Chris Judah-Lauder
Margaret Campbelle-Holman	Carol King
Emily Crocker	Vincent P. Lawrence
Marilyn C. Davidson	Ellen McCullough-Brabson
Robert de Frece	Janet McMillion
Virginia Ebinger	Nancy L.T. Miller
Mary Goetze	Ivy Rawlins
Betsy M. Henderson	Susan Snyder
John Jacobson	Gilberto D. Soto

Kodály Contributing Consultant
Sr. Lorna Zemke

Mc Graw Hill **Macmillan McGraw-Hill**

INTRODUCTION

This *Teacher's Resource Masters* book contains supplementary activities for *Spotlight on Music*. These Resource Masters include the following:

- A variety of activities that reinforce or review concepts taught in the lessons. Some Resource Masters emphasize manipulative activities, while others offer opportunities for written or aural activities.

- Student and teacher support to complete the Creative Unit Projects. Students can use the Resource Masters to guide them through the project and complete a self-assessment at the project's conclusion. Teachers are also given an assessment rubric for each Creative Unit Project.

- Listening maps that provide visual guidance for students as they listen to specific music selections. The listening maps help students identify melodic and rhythmic patterns, tone color, form, and other musical elements. Suggestions for how to use these listening maps in the classroom are provided at the beginning of the Listening Map section.

- Review questions for each unit. The Spotlight Your Success! Resource Masters allow students to record their responses to the review questions at the completion of each unit. The Read and Listen questions and music examples are recorded.

- Scripts and lyrics for the musical theater Broadway for Kids.

- Sign language versions of selected songs using American Sign Language.

All Resource Masters may be duplicated for classroom use. Each Resource Master is cross referenced to a specific unit and lesson that it was designed to support.

ACKNOWLEDGMENTS

Grateful acknowledgment is given to the following publishers. Every effort has been made to trace the ownership of all copyrighted material and to secure the necessary permissions to reprint these selections. In the case of some selections for which acknowledgment is not given, extensive research has failed to locate the copyright holders.

Schoolhouse Rock Live! Junior
Originally Adapted for the Stage by Theater BAM
From the Series Created by George Newall and Tom Yohe
Based on an Idea by David McCall
Book by Scott Ferguson, George Keating, and Kyle Hall
Music and Lyrics by Lynn Ahrens, Bob Dorough, Dave Frishberg, Kathy Mandry, George Newall, and Tom Yohe

© Music and Lyrics 1995 and TM American Broadcasting Companies, Inc.
The above copyright notice may be subject to change to conform to new or different requirements upon written notification from:
American Broadcasting Companies, Inc.
Book © Theatre BAM
International Copyright Secured. All Rights Reserved.
Schoolhouse Rock Live! Junior Libretto/Vocal book © 2001 by MTI Enterprises, Inc.
Broadway Junior and **The Broadway Junior Collection** are trademarks of MTI Enterprises, Inc.

TABLE OF CONTENTS

SPOTLIGHT ON CONCEPTS

UNIT ❶ ───────────────────────────────── PAGE

1-1	School-to-Home Letter: English and Spanish	1
1-2	Creative Unit Project	3
1-3	Creative Unit Project	4
1-4	I've Got Rhythm	5
1-5	Listen Up!	6
1-6	Rhythm and Rhyme	7
1-7	Join the Staff	8
1-8	Mid-Unit Review	9
1-9	Character Instruments	10
1-10	Applause, Applause	11
1-11	Make Your Own Music	12
1-12	Spotlight Your Success!	13
1-13	Self-Assessment	15
1-14	Teacher Assessment	16

UNIT ❷ ───────────────────────────────── PAGE

2-1	School-to-Home Letter: English and Spanish	17
2-2	Creative Unit Project	19
2-3	Creative Unit Project	20
2-4	Form a Poem	21
2-5	Song and Dance	22
2-6	Perfect Pitch	23
2-7	Clap in Time	24
2-8	Mid-Unit Review	25
2-9	A Hero for All Times	26
2-10	Time through Time	27
2-11	Eight-Beat Rhythms	28
2-12	Spotlight Your Success!	29
2-13	Self-Assessment	31
2-14	Teacher Assessment	32

UNIT ❸ ───────────────────────────────── PAGE

3-1	School-to-Home Letter: English and Spanish	33
3-2	Creative Unit Project	35
3-3	Creative Unit Project	36
3-4	Playing the Piper	37
3-5	Your Very Own Treasures	38
3-6	Throw It Out the Window	39
3-7	Name That Pitch	40
3-8	Mid-Unit Review	41
3-9	Samba!	42
3-10	These Fish Have Notes	43

3-11	Spotlight Your Success!	45
3-12	Self-Assessment	47
3-13	Teacher Assessment	48

UNIT (4) ——————————————— PAGE

4-1	School-to-Home Letter: English and Spanish	49
4-2	Creative Unit Project	51
4-3	Creative Unit Project	52
4-4	Alike or Not?	52
4-5	Don't Lose That Beat	54
4-6	Quarter, Eighth, Sixteenth	55
4-7	*Penta* Means "Five"	56
4-8	Mid-Unit Review	57
4-9	Repeated Notes, Steps, and Skips	58
4-10	A Musical Conversation	59
4-11	Rondo on the Road	60
4-12	Spotlight Your Success!	61
4-13	Self-Assessment	63
4-14	Teacher Assessment	64

UNIT (5) ——————————————— PAGE

5-1	School-to-Home Letter: English and Spanish	65
5-2	Creative Unit Project	67
5-3	Creative Unit Project	68
5-4	Think in Threes	69
5-5	Repeated Rhythms	70
5-6	The Maori People	71
5-7	The Conductor's Job	72
5-8	Mid-Unit Review	73
5-9	Melodic Ostinato	74
5-10	The Shepherd and His Sheep	75
5-11	Around and Around	76
5-12	Spotlight Your Success!	77
5-13	Self-Assessment	79
5-14	Teacher Assessment	80

UNIT (6) ——————————————— PAGE

6-1	School-to-Home Letter: English and Spanish	81
6-2	Creative Unit Project	83
6-3	Creative Unit Project	84
6-4	Rounding the Bases	85
6-5	Getting Centered	86
6-6	Dancing with Props	87
6-7	Pitches and Centers	88
6-8	Mid-Unit Review	89
6-9	Speed It Up	90
6-10	Make Your Marks	91
6-11	Rearranging Rhythms	92

6-12	Spotlight Your Success!	93
6-13	Self-Assessment	95
6-14	Teacher Assessment	96

SPOTLIGHT ON MUSIC READING

R-1	Quarter and Eighth Notes	97
R-2	Melodic Steps and Skips	98
R-3	Composing a Melody	99
R-4	Composing with *So* and *La*	100
R-5	Improvising "Morning Music"	101
R-6	Writing *Do, Re, Mi, So, La*	102
R-7	Find the Pitch	103
R-8	Low *La*	104
R-9	Conducting in $\frac{2}{4}$	105
R-10	Writing Low *So* and *La*	106
R-11	Melody in $\frac{2}{2}$	107
R-12	Sixteenth Notes	108
R-13	Write the Missing *Do*	109
R-14	High *Do*	110
R-15	Writing High *Do*	111
R-16	Find the Missing *Do*	112
R-17	On the Upbeat	113
R-18	Whole Notes	114
R-19	Dotted Half Notes	115
R-20	Playing an Ostinato	116
R-21	Bugle Calls	117
R-22	Compose and Improvise	118
R-23	ABA Form	119
R-24	Ties and Slurs	120
R-25	Beat Bars	121
R-26	Pitch Ladder	122
R-27	Curwen Hand Signals	123
R-28	Scale Stairs	124
R-29	Pitch Xylophone	125
R-30	Scale Brackets	126

SPOTLIGHT ON PERFORMANCE

P-1	*Schoolhouse Rock Live!* Script and Lyrics	127
P-2	There Was an Old Lady	139
P-3	The Gebeta Board	141
P-4	Isabela and the Troll	143
P-5	Sad Sack Song	145
P-6	Happy Sack Song	146

SPOTLIGHT ON CELEBRATIONS

C-1	Patriotic Words	147
C-2	Hispanic Heritage	148
C-3	Fall Harvest Feasts	149
C-4	Scary Clues	150
C-5	Winter Festivals	151
C-6	"I Have a Dream"	152
C-7	Chinese New Year	153
C-8	An Irish Tale	154
C-9	Celebrate the Earth	155
C-10	Cinco de Mayo	156

LISTENING MAPS

	Listening Map Instructions	157
LM-3	Guadalquivir	160
LM-4	Pata Pata	161
LM-6	A Clock at Night	162
LM-8	Les saluts	163
LM-11	Trio for Piano, Violin, and Cello No. 39, Finale ("Gypsy Rondo")	164
LM-13	Gigue from Suite No. 1 for Cello	165
LM-14	La raspa	166
LM-19	Brafferton Village/Walsh's Hornpipe	167

SPOTLIGHT ON SIGNING

	Introduction to Signed Songs	168
S-1	Alphabet and Numbers	169
S-2	Yellow Submarine	170
S-3	This Is America	171
S-4	Eight Days of Hanukkah	173
S-5	Shalom Chaveyrim	176
S-6	Consider Yourself	177
S-7	Evergreen, Everblue	181
S-8	Colors of the Wind	183
S-9	Rise Up Singin'	186

| | Answer Key | 188 |

Name _____ Date _____

School-to-Home Letter

Dear Family,

What an exciting, musical school year is in store for your third grader! This year your child will continue to learn new skills and concepts that will form the foundation for a lifetime of musical enjoyment.

In this first unit, your child will learn to play a movement game and a counting game with music. Through poetry he or she will begin to explore the concepts of rhythm and beat, learning how rhythm is written in musical pieces by using a staff with measures, notes, and rests. Listening to and singing traditional melodies from different cultures will serve as an introduction to pitch *(do, re, mi)* and to the special sounds—tone color—of various instruments. These songs also highlight the universal nature of music. At home, you can reinforce your child's learning by sharing music that you love.

I am here to help you help your child explore our musical world. Producing a music program at school requires much work and many hands. Thank you for whatever assistance you can offer this year: at home, at school, or both. Together we can create a musical learning experience for your child that will enrich his or her life for many years to come.

Sincerely,

Third Grade Music Teacher

Nombre: _____ Fecha: _____

School-to-Home Letter

Estimada Familia:

¡Qué año tan emocionante le espera a su hijo de tercer grado en la clase de música! Este año su hijo continuará aprendiendo nuevas habilidades y conceptos que constituirán los cimientos para que disfrute de la música toda la vida.

En esta primera unidad, su hijo aprenderá a jugar un juego de movimientos y un juego de conteo con la música. Mediante la poesía él o ella comenzará a explorar los conceptos del ritmo y compás, aprendiendo el modo en que se escribe el ritmo en las piezas musicales utilizando un pentagrama con medidas, notas y silencios (pausas). Escuchar y cantar melodías tradicionales de diferentes culturas servirá como introducción a los tonos (*do, re, mi*) y a los sonidos especiales—el color del tono—de varios instrumentos. Estas canciones también destacan la naturaleza universal de la música. En su hogar, usted puede reforzar el aprendizaje de su hijo/a compartiendo música que usted ama.

Estoy aquí para ayudar a su hijo a explorar nuestro mundo musical. Hacer un programa de música en la escuela requiere mucho trabajo y muchas manos. Le agradecemos cualquier colaboración que nos pueda ofrecer durante este año: desde su hogar, en la escuela o en ambos lugares. Juntos podemos crear una experiencia musical de aprendizaje para su hijo o hija que enriquecerá su vida en los años venideros.

Atentamente,

Maestra de Música de Tercer Grado

Name _____ Date _____

Creative Unit Project

Your project for Unit 1 is to make up a game. You will use speech and rhythm patterns to teach something. Follow the steps below.

STEP 1 (after Lesson 1)
What would you like your game to teach? With your group, make a list of ideas. Would you like to teach state names? Would you like to teach someone to count in Spanish? Write all of your ideas. Circle the group's favorite idea.

_____

_____

_____

_____

STEP 2 (after Lesson 2)
Now list words that fit your topic. You need to choose four words that you will teach. For example, if you are teaching state names, you might choose four states that start with the letter M (Massachusetts, Michigan, Missouri, Montana). Write down everyone's ideas. Put a star next to the four words you choose. Say the words in rhythm. Clap along.

_____

_____

_____

_____

Creative Unit Project

RESOURCE MASTER 1•3

STEP 3 (after Lesson 3)
Remember your game words and rhythm. Make up a movement pattern to the rhythm of the words. Use body percussion. Here are some ideas to try.
- Clap
- Snap
- Pat legs
- Tap head
- Tap shoulders

You might speak a word and then do a movement. Or you might speak the words while you do the body percussion. Figure out what works best to keep a steady beat going. After you decide on a final movement pattern, practice as a group. Work on staying together.

STEP 4 (after Lesson 4)
Continue practicing as a group. If you want to make your game longer, add four more words and repeat the movements.
(Look at your list of words in Step 2.)

Practice for your performance. Remember these goals:
- Keep a steady beat.
- Match the body percussion to the rhythm of the words.
- Make it a fun way to learn!

I've Got Rhythm

Read the poem. Note the words and syllables that are underlined.
These words show the beat of the poem.

From Windy Nights
by Robert Louis Stevenson

When-<u>ev</u>-er the <u>moon</u> and <u>stars</u> are <u>set</u>,

   When-<u>ev</u>-er the <u>wind</u> is <u>high</u>,

<u>All</u> night <u>long</u> in the <u>dark</u> and <u>wet</u>,

   A <u>man</u> goes <u>rid</u>-ing <u>by</u>.

<u>Late</u> in the <u>night</u> when the <u>fires</u> are <u>out</u>,

<u>Why</u> does he <u>gal</u>-lop and <u>gal</u>-lop a-<u>bout</u>?

Now show the rhythm of the poem.
Write long and short rhythm bars above each line.

   When-ev-er the moon and stars are set,

     When-ev-er the wind is high,

   All night long in the dark and wet,

     A man goes rid-ing by.

   Late in the night when the fires are out,

     Why does he gal-lop and gal-lop a-bout?

Listen Up!

Listen to the song "I's the B'y." Cut out the four lines of melodies below. Sing each line to yourself as you cut it out.

1.

2.

3.

4.

Now listen to the song again. This time, match each printed line on your desk to the sung line. Arrange the lines in the correct order on your desk.

Take a blank sheet of paper. Paste the lines in the correct order on the paper.

Listen to the song a third time. Make sure that the printed lines are in the same order as the lines you hear sung.

Name _____ Date _____

Rhythm and Rhyme

1. Circle the quarter note.

a. 　　　　b. ♩̸　　　　c. ♩

2. Box the beamed eighth notes.

a. ♫　　　　b. ♩̸　　　　c. ♩

3. Circle the rhythm that matches the rhythm of the
words *pumpkin pie.*

a. ♫　　　　b. ♫ ♩　　　　c. ♫ ♫

4. Write the rhythm of the second line of the song "Great Big House."

Fill in each blank with a quarter note (♩), eighth notes (♫), or a

quarter rest (♩̸).

____　　_____　　_____　　____

　Ev'ry　　　room that　　　I　been　　　in,

_____　　_____　　_____

　Filled with　　　pump-kin　　　pie.

Join the Staff

1. Look at these pitch syllables from "The Happy Wanderer."

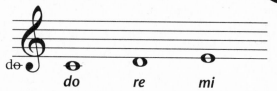

Write *do, re,* or *mi* below each note.

a.

c.

b.

d.

Write the letter to match the *do re mi* syllables with the notation.

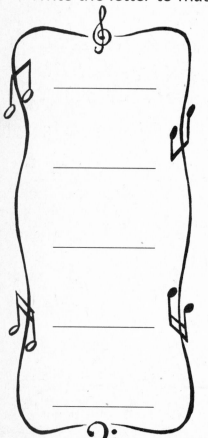

_____ **2.** *mi mi do*

_____ **3.** *do re mi*

_____ **4.** *mi mi mi*

_____ **5.** *mi re do*

_____ **6.** *do re do*

a.

b.

c.

d.

e.

Name _____ Date _____

Mid-Unit Review

Complete the puzzle.
Use words you have learned.

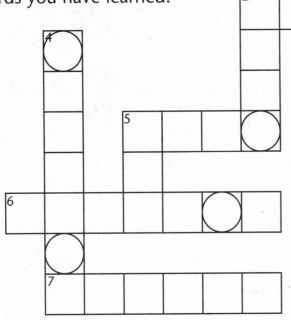

Across

2. Long and short sounds in music are its _____.

5. You can tap out the _____ to a song.

6. A _____ note has a stem but no beam.

7. Two _____ notes make a quarter note.

Down

1. You write notes on a _____.

2. You don't sing when the music calls for a _____.

3. _____ is another word for *tune*.

4. The space between bars is a _____.

5. A _____ line goes up and down on a staff.

Write the letters that are circled in the puzzle in the order in which they appear—left to right and top to bottom. You will spell out a word that has to do with beat.

____ ____ ____ ____ ____ ____

Character Instruments

Do people's voices sometimes make you think of musical instruments? Does your gym teacher blast like a trumpet? Does your little sister ever pipe like a flute? Does your uncle roar like a tuba?

Think of a story, a TV show, or a comic strip that you like. List the main characters. Decide what instrument each character sounds like. Write the name of the instrument next to each character's name. Then tell why you chose each instrument.

Title _____

Main Character	Instrument
_____	_____
_____	_____
_____	_____
_____	_____
_____	_____
_____	_____

Name _____ Date _____

Applause, Applause

RESOURCE MASTER

Match each rhythm line with the song from which it comes. Write the letter of the correct title next to each line.

a. "Simon Says"	**d.** "I's the B'y"	**g.** "The Happy Wanderer"
b. "Billy"	**e.** "Great Big House"	**h.** "Egy Üveg Alma"
c. "Chan Mali Chan"	**f.** "Sweet Potatoes"	**i.** "De Aquel Cerro"

____ 1.

____ 2.

____ 3.

____ 4.

____ 5.

____ 6.

____ 7.

____ 8.

____ 9.

Make Your Own Music

Use what you know about rhythms to make your own music.
Create a rhythm piece that has eight beats in all.

1. Use ♩ , ♫ , and 𝄽

2. Choose your own order for the beats of your rhythm.

3. Write your rhythm in the space below.

4. Use the meter signature ₂/₄ for your rhythm pattern.

5. Make sure that each measure has two beats.

6. Share your music with the class!
   You can clap it, speak it, or play it
   on a rhythm instrument.

Spotlight Your Success! RESOURCE MASTER

Review Circle the correct answer.

1. What do you call a group of pitches that moves upward, downward, or stays the same?
a. pitch   b. melody   c. rhythm   d. beat

2. If the meter signature of a song is $\frac{2}{4}$, how many beats are in the measure?
a. 3   b. 8   c. 4   d. 2

3. This staff shows the pitches *mi, re,* and *do.*

How does this melody move?
a. upward   b. downward   c. stays the same

Read and Listen Circle the correct answer.

1. Read these rhythms. Then listen. Which rhythm do you hear?

2. Listen to the melody. With your index finger, trace the shape of the melody in the air. How did the melody move?
a. upward   b. downward   c. stayed the same

Spotlight Your Success! RESOURCE MASTER 1·12

3. Read these melodies with *do, re,* and *mi.* Listen to the melody. Which melody do you hear?

a.

c.

b.

Think! Write your answers. Use your own paper.

1. How do beat and rhythm of the words differ?

2. The shape of a melody moves upward. How would the pitches of the melody appear on a musical staff?

3. Write about the tone color of an instrument you like.

Create and Perform   Create your own melody.

1. Use $\overset{2}{\mathrm{P}}$ for your meter signature.

2. Use ♩, ♫ ♩, and 𝄽 to create your rhythm pattern.

3. Use *mi, re,* and *do* for your pitches.

4. Write your music on the staff.

5. Quietly practice what you wrote.

Name _____ Date _____

Self-Assessment

Who worked with you on the unit project? Write everyone's name.

_____   _____

_____   _____

What did you like best about the project? _____

_____

What did you like least? _____

_____

If you could do the project again, what would you change? _____

_____

How did your group do during the performance?
The three goals for the project are listed below.
Put an X in the box that shows how you did.

Goal	😁	🙂	😐	🙁
Our group kept a steady beat.				
Our body percussion matched the rhythm of the words.				
Our group stayed together.				

Teacher Assessment

RESOURCE MASTER

	Steady Tempo	Body Percussion/ Rhythm of the Words	Ensemble
Excellent	Consistently kept a steady tempo throughout the performance.	Body percussion matched all of the rhythm of the words accurately.	Performed together as an ensemble without teacher assistance.
*Competent	Kept a steady tempo through most of the performance.	Body percussion matched almost all of the rhythm of the words.	Performed together as an ensemble with minimal teacher assistance.
Progressing	Kept a steady tempo through some of the performance.	Body percussion matched some of the rhythm of the words.	Performed together as an ensemble with moderate teacher assistance.
Showing Little Progress	Kept a steady tempo during very little of the performance.	Body percussion matched little of the rhythm of the words.	Performed together as an ensemble with considerable teacher assistance.

Not Scorable: Did not participate.

*Competent is the expected level for all students.

Note to teacher: Have students vote on whether the game was fun to do.

School-to-Home Letter

Dear Family,

How often are you aware of the sounds of music all around you? This unit draws musical inspiration from everyday life and nature.

Seeing the forms, or patterns, in songs makes them easier to learn. Your child will start to recognize the form of a song by assigning letters to its sections. For example, if a song has two sections that are the same, its form is written as A A . If a song has two distinct sections, such as a verse and a chorus, its form is written as A B.

In this unit students will also reinforce their understanding of rhythm by clapping and playing rhythms on instruments. Half notes now join quarter and eighth notes in song measures. The importance of tempo, or pace, is illustrated in a song about a clock. Your student will also add the pitches *so* and *la* to the pitches *do, re,* and *mi* that were presented in Unit 1.

The concept of countermelody—a separate melody that fits with the main one—appears. The concept of dynamics—how loud or soft a piece of music should be played or sung—is also introduced.

As in the first unit, songs from all around the world stress the universality of music and serve as windows into diverse cultures. The potential for you and your child to enjoy the pleasure of music is boundless!

Sincerely,

Third Grade Music Teacher

School-to-Home Letter

Estimada Familia:

¿Con qué frecuencia tiene conciencia de los sonidos musicales que lo rodean? Esta unidad toma su inspiración musical de varios lugares que se encuentran en la vida diaria y en la naturaleza.

Ver las formas, o patrones, en las canciones hace que éstas sean más fáciles de aprender. Su hijo comenzará a reconocer la forma de una canción asignándole letras a sus partes. Por ejemplo, si una canción tiene dos partes que son iguales, su forma se escribe como A A. Si la canción tiene dos partes distintas, como por ejemplo verso y un coro, su forma se escribe como A B.

En esta unidad los alumnos también reforzarán su comprensión del ritmo aplaudiendo y tamborileando los ritmos sobre los instrumentos. Las medias notas ahora se unen a las negras y las corcheas en la medición. La importancia del tempo, o ritmo, se ilustra en una canción sobre un reloj. Su hijo también agregará tonos *sol* y *la* y los tonos *do, re,* y *mi* que se presentaron en la Unidad 1.

El concepto de contramelodía —una melodía separada que encaja con la principal—aparece. También se introduce el concepto de dinámica —cuán fuerte o leve debe ejecutarse o cantarse una pieza musical.

Como en la primera unidad, las canciones de todo el mundo enfatizan la universalidad de la música y sirven como puerta a las diversas culturas. El potencial para usted y para su hijo o hija para disfrutar del placer de la música, es ilimitado

Atentamente,

Maestra de Música de Tercer Grado

Creative Unit Project

RESOURCE MASTER

For your Unit 2 project, you will create an ABA piece. Your group will compose a rhythm pattern and a melody to go with a poem. Then you will perform your piece. Follow the steps below.

STEP 1 (after Lesson 1)

• Read the poem "City Music," page 74 of your music book. Talk with your group about the poem's meaning. Then each of you should write one sentence about the meaning. Use the index cards given to you by your teacher.

• Speak the poem aloud. Match how you speak to the meaning of the poem. Use this meter: ♩ . Get louder or softer, faster or slower.

STEP 2 (after Lesson 2)

• Have each group member draw four beat bars on a card, as in this example.

• Now you should each create a four-beat rhythm. Write the notes above the beat bars.

• Share your rhythm patterns. Have one group member pat, snap, or clap a steady beat. Have another group member clap his or her four-beat pattern.

• As a group, choose your two favorite patterns. One will be for the A section of your piece. The other will be for the B section. Practice clapping the two patterns. Repeat each pattern four times. Have one person keep a steady beat on a hand drum.

Name _____ Date _____

Creative Unit Project RESOURCE MASTER 2•3

STEP 3 (after Lesson 3)
• Review your four-beat rhythm pattern for the B section of your piece. Write a melody to go with it. Use only *mi, so,* and *la.*

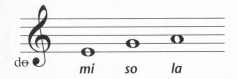

• Write the pitch syllables for your melody on the card with the B rhythm pattern.
• Practice the melody. Have one group member pat a steady beat. Try singing the melody through four times. Use good breath support.

STEP 4 (after Lesson 4)
• Review the poem "City Music." Would you like to add found sounds to your piece? These could help get across the meaning. You could add found sounds to your B section. Try it out. Also practice getting louder and softer during this section. If you need help staying on pitch, use an alto xylophone.
• Practice your A section as well. Some of the group should play the rhythm patterns while others speak the poem.

STEP 5 (after Lesson 5)
• Now it's time to put your whole piece together. Practice the A and B sections. Then practice them in the correct form: ABA. Work on moving smoothly between the sections.
• Throughout your piece, remember to breathe correctly. Get louder or softer, faster or slower, to show the poem's meaning. Work on staying together.
• Keep practicing until you're ready to perform!

Name _____ Date _____

Form a Poem

You've learned that a song or other piece of music follows a plan. That plan is called its form. Poems have forms, too.

Haiku is a Japanese form of poetry. Haiku used to be about only nature. Now it can be about anything.

A haiku has three lines that don't rhyme. Think of the lines as three sections. The first and third sections have five syllables. The second, or middle, section has seven syllables. You can write its form as A B A. Here are two examples of haiku.

Watchers
One hundred starlings
Perching on telephone wires—
Sharp-eyed observers.

The Clown
A broad painted smile,
Silly clothes, and outsized feet
Hide sadness within.

Now think of a subject for a haiku. Write your own haiku on the lines below. Then give it a title.

_____

_____

_____

_____

Song and Dance

RESOURCE MASTER

Native Americans have gathered to perform music and dances for centuries. This is a way they share their culture.

Sun Dance

The sun dance was the most important part of the Plains Indians' religion in the nineteenth century. At the beginning of summer, each nation held a sun dance that lasted more than four days. The dance showed that all of nature is connected. The best lodge (house) builder was in charge of building the lodge for the dance. A pole with a buffalo head was put in the center of the lodge to honor the buffalo. The Plains Indians honored the buffalo because they used it for their food, shelter, and clothing.

White Deer Dance

This dance comes from the Yurok people of northern California. It was a form of prayer asking for enough food for the year. Around the full moon in September, the medicine man led 30 men in the dance. They danced for three days. The dancers wore deerskin skirts trimmed with shells and necklaces made from shells and beads. They held sticks covered with deerskin and moved the sticks in special ways as they danced.

Southern Straight Dance

Southern nations performed a dance that told the story of a hunting trip or a war party. The dancers pretended to follow the trail of an animal or an enemy. They often wore a porcupine headdress and an otter's tail. Songs for this dance could be made up right before the dance or could be many years old.

On a separate sheet of paper, draw a picture of a dancer performing one of these dances. Title your drawing.

Perfect Pitch

Look at the staff. It shows where *do* is in the song "El florón."
From it you can figure out where other notes are in the song.

1. Match the pitch names to the staff notation. Write the letters in the blanks.

a. *do mi so mi do* _____

b. *so mi re do so* _____

c. *la la mi so re* _____

2. Write the notes to match the pitch names.

a.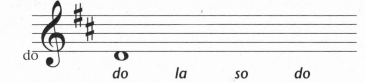
  do la so do

b.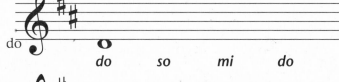
  do so mi do

c.
  mi re mi so

d.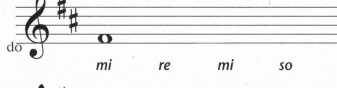
  so do mi re

Clap in Time

Cut apart the flash cards along the dotted lines. Work with a partner. Place one set of flash cards face up on a desk or table. One partner is the "rhythm master." He or she claps out the rhythm of one of the flash cards. The other partner picks up the correct card. Then switch roles, and play again.

Mid-Unit Review

RESOURCE MASTER 2•8

Complete the sentences by writing the correct word in the blank.

1. A separate melody that fits with the main melody is called a
_____.

2. A note that has the same length as two quarter notes is a
_____.

3. The plan that a piece of music follows is called its _____.

4. A song with two sections that are the same has a form that
can be written _____.

5. A song with two sections that are different has a form that
can be written _____.

Write the correct notes on each staff above the pitch syllables.

6.
do   re   mi   re   mi   so

7.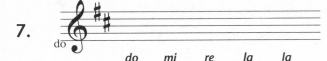
do   do   mi   re   la   la

8.
do   mi   re   so   mi   re

9.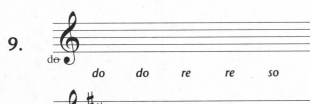
do   do   do   re   re   so

10.
do   do   mi   so   la   mi

A Hero for All Times

RESOURCE MASTER 2•9

An opera is a play in which all the parts are sung. An orchestra plays the music. The singers wear costumes, and the stage has special scenery.

William Tell is a popular opera written by Gioacchino Rossini. He was an Italian who lived from 1792 to 1868. Read the story of the opera below in words and pictures.

Around 1200 Switzerland was ruled by a cruel Austrian governor named Gessler. The Swiss people wanted to be free from Austria. William Tell led their fight.

To show that he was very powerful, Gessler hung his on a | . He

ordered everyone to to it. William Tell refused. Gessler decided to

punish Tell. Gessler ordered Tell to take his \ and  and shoot an

 off his son's . William Tell shot his and split the in two.

He became a hero and helped the Swiss people get their freedom.

An overture is a musical introduction to an opera. Its melodies are from the opera. The *William Tell Overture* has four parts. They paint musical pictures. The parts are listed below. What kind of instruments would you use in each section?

"At Dawn" _____   "The Storm" _____

"The Calm" _____   "Call to Arms" _____

Name _____ Date _____

Time through Time

Ever since people first danced, they have used a beat to know when to step. Music for listening needs a beat, too.

Early people used whatever was handy to keep a beat. It could be hitting sticks on stones, clapping their hands, or clicking their tongues.

Later people began to make instruments that could be used to keep a beat. A piece of metal could be struck with another. Animal skins were stretched to make drums. Rattles were made from dried gourds.

When musicians formed large orchestras many centuries later, a conductor helped them keep time. When practicing, a musician might use a metronome. It is a small timer that can be set to a certain beat. It goes *tick, tick, tick* to help the musician stay on beat.

Think of a simple instrument you would like to use to keep time. On another piece of paper, draw a picture that shows how you would make it.

Optional Activity: Make your instrument. Get together with other students, and use your instruments to provide the beat for songs and dances in your class.

Eight-Beat Rhythms

RESOURCE MASTER **2•11**

Create an eight-beat rhythm with a partner. Use the word cards below. Add them to your partner's.

Say and clap *rattle* for eighth notes (♪♪).

Say and clap *chirp* for quarter notes (♩).

Brush and say *scratch* for half notes (♩).

With your partner, arrange your rhythm in different ways. Say your rhythm with a steady tempo. Perform your eight-beat rhythm for the class.

scratch	scratch

chirp	chirp

rattle	rattle

Name _____ Date _____

Spotlight Your Success! RESOURCE MASTER 2•12

Review

Circle the correct answer.

1. Which pattern has half notes?

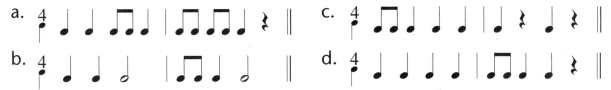

2. The first pitch is *do.* Where is *la?*

a. first space   b. second space   c. third line

3. Why are some sections of music called B?

a. The B section is just like the A section.

b. The B section is different from the A section.

c. The B section is a big section.

Read and Listen

Circle the correct answer.

1. Listen to an example with three sections. Close your eyes. Raise your hand each time you hear the A section. Fold your arms each time you hear the B section. What is the form?

a. AAB   b. ABB   c. ABA

2. Read these melodies with ♩, ♩, and ♩♩ Listen to the melody. Which melody do you hear?

Spotlight Your Success! RESOURCE MASTER 2•12

Think! Write your answers. Use your own paper.

1. What is the difference between *piano* and *forte*?

2. When you are learning to sing a new piece, what tempo would you choose?

3. What would the form be if only contrast were used in a three section piece of music?

4. Write about how dynamics change the feeling of a song.

Create and Perform

Create a rhythm with ABA as the form.

1. Use ♩⁴ for your meter signature.

2. Make each section eight beats long.

3 Use at least one ♩ in each section.

4. Write your rhythm below.

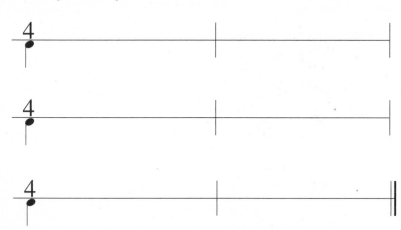

5. Play your rhythm.

Name _____ Date _____

Self-Assessment

Who worked with you on the unit project? Write everyone's name.

_____   _____

_____   _____

What did you like best about the project? _____

_____

What did you like least? _____

_____

If you could do the project again, what would you change? _____

_____

How did your group do during the performance?
The goals for the project are listed below.
Put an X in the box that shows how you did.

Goal	😁	🙂	😐	🙁
Our group used good breathing.				
We got louder and softer, faster and slower, to help show the poem's meaning.				
Our group stayed together.				

Name _____ Date _____

Teacher Assessment

RESOURCE MASTER 2•14

	Breath Support	Dynamics	Group Participation
Excellent	Sang with excellent breath support.	Performed the dynamics extremely well and in balance with others in the group.	All students participated and contributed to the group process throughout the project.
*Competent	Sang with good breath support.	Performed the dynamics well and mostly in balance with others in the group.	Almost all students participated and contributed to the group process throughout the project.
Progressing	Sang with partially sufficient breath support.	Performed the dynamics fairly well and somewhat in balance with others in the group.	Some students participated and contributed to the group process throughout the project, but some did not.
Showing Little Progress	Sang with limited breath support.	Attempted to perform the dynamics in balance with others in the group, but effort was not very successful.	Few students participated and contributed to the group process throughout the project.

Not Scorable: Did not participate.

*Competent is the expected level for all students.

USE WITH GRADE 3, UNIT 2, CREATIVE UNIT PROJECT

Name _____ Date _____

School-to-Home Letter

Dear Family,

This unit reinforces the idea that people from every land and culture share our planet and are deserving of respect. In fact, the opening song, "Colors of the Wind" from the movie *Pocahontas,* tells us that we should respect every *thing* on the planet as well.

Your student is encouraged to treasure your family traditions—the stories and customs that have been passed down through generations. Lively Native American and Scottish songs with rhythmic dances introduce this idea. A song called "Treasure Chests" is about this topic. The unit's stories and songs come from a variety of traditions, and students will learn song lyrics in several different languages.

In this unit your child will learn about musical phrases: those groups of notes that make up a musical thought. He or she will examine songs with two sections, a verse section and a refrain section. The refrain is sung after each of the verses. Your child will have the opportunity to write his or her own verse to a rousing nonsense song.

Here the study of rhythm is broadened, as your student compares different rhythm patterns. Pitch is also continued, with the introduction of the pitches low *so* and low *la.*

Songs with first and second endings appear, with a repeat sign indicating that a section of music is sung or played again.

Finally, your child is invited to be his or her own choreographer by creating movements to accompany a song. After all, music is not just for playing or singing, but also for dancing! Join in the musical fun with your child.

Sincerely,

Third Grade Music Teacher

School-to-Home Letter

Estimada Familia:

Esta unidad refuerza la idea de que la gente de cualquier lugar y cultura comparte un planeta y merece respeto. De hecho, la canción de apertura, "*Colors of the Wind*" de la película *Pocahontas,* nos dice que debemos respetar a cada cosa de este planeta también.

Se alienta a su hijo a que atesore las tradiciones familiares historias y costumbres que se han transmitido de generación en generación. Las animadas canciones de los indios americanos y las canciones escocesas con sus danzas rítmicas presentan ese concepto. Una canción llamada "Treasure Chests" trata sobre este tema. Las historias y las canciones de esta unidad provienen de una variedad de tradiciones y los alumnos aprenderán las letras de las canciones en varios idiomas diferentes.

En esta unidad su hijo aprenderá sobre las frases musicales: esos grupos de notas que conforman un pensamiento musical. Examinarán canciones con dos secciones: la sección del verso y la sección del estribillo. El estribillo se canta luego de los versos. Su hijo tendrá la oportunidad de escribir sus propios versos a una "motivadora canción sin ton ni son".

Se amplía aquí el estudio del ritmo a medida que su hijo compara diferentes esquemas rítmicos. Se continúa con el tono, añadiendo los tonos bajos *so y la.*

Aparecen canciones con primera y segunda terminación, con un signo que se repite para indicar que una sección de la música se canta o se toca nuevamente.

Por último, se invita a su hijo a que sea su propio coreógrafo creando movimientos para acompañar la canción. Después de todo, la música no es simplemente para tocar o para cantar, ¡también es para bailar! Únase con su hijo o hija a la diversión musical.

Atentamente,

Maestra de Música de Tercer Grado

Creative Unit Project

RESOURCE MASTER

For your Unit 3 project, your group will write song lyrics. The lyrics will go with a tune you already know. The lyrics will tell something interesting about your school. You will perform the song at the end of the unit. Follow these steps.

STEP 1 (after Lesson 1)
Start by deciding what you would like to know about your school. Make a list of questions you would like to answer. For each question, figure out how you can find out the answer. Circle the questions that you will be most likely to answer. Make a plan for finding the information.

_____

_____

_____

_____

_____

You can also begin to think about a tune that you all know. Hum the melody together. Clap the rhythm.

STEP 2 (after Lesson 2)
Organize the information you have found. Turn it into lyrics for the tune you have chosen. Remember that the lyrics have to match the rhythm. Try speaking the words aloud to the rhythm. One group member can clap a steady beat. Keep working on the words until they fit the melody. Then write the lyrics on the next page.

Creative Unit Project

RESOURCE MASTER

[ ]

STEP 3 (after Lesson 3)

Now practice singing your lyrics to the song. Have one group member pat a steady beat. Listen carefully as you sing.

- Do the lyrics match the rhythm of the song?
- Are you saying the words clearly?
- Are you all staying together?

Keep practicing. Change the lyrics if you need to!

STEP 4 (after Lesson 4)

Keep practicing your song. If you would like, add some special elements. Here are some ideas.

- Movements
- Costumes
- Props

Think about how to help the audience understand the information about your school. Think about how to make the performance interesting. Keep practicing until you feel confident. Then you are ready to perform!

Name _____ Date _____

Playing the Piper

The pipes are calling—the bagpipes, that is. Do you think of the bagpipe as a Scottish instrument? You're right, but only partly.

Bagpipes have been around since the time of the ancient Greeks and Romans. Bagpipe playing later spread across Europe. By the Middle Ages, the bagpipe was one of the most popular instruments. Minstrels played bagpipes as they wandered through the countryside and into village squares.

When cities began to grow, much music-making moved indoors. People began to invent new instruments. In most places the bagpipe became less popular. But in Scotland it is still played often. Scottish people brought the bagpipe to the United States. At many big parades you can hear the pipes a-piping.

How hard is it to learn to play the bagpipe? A piper must send a steady flow of air through the blowpipe to the bag. Then two other kinds of pipes receive the air blown into the bag. The chanter pipe plays the melody. It has finger holes to change notes. The drone pipes are tuned to certain notes. The bagpipe is not easy to learn, but practice and patience pay off.

If you could play the bagpipe, where would you play it—and why? On a separate sheet of paper, write a paragraph about this. Then draw a picture of yourself playing the bagpipe in that place.

Name _____ Date _____

Your Very Own Treasures

RESOURCE MASTER 3•5

Do you remember the song "Treasure Chests"? The notes below show the rhythm of the first two lines of the verses. (The notes do not show the rhythm of the words "And ways to get along; and ways to get along.")

Think of things that you treasure from your family's culture. Using the rhythm from the song, write your own words to the second verse of "Treasure Chests." Write the words below each line of notes.

38

USE WITH GRADE 3, UNIT 3, LESSON 2

Name _____ Date _____

Throw It Out the Window

See if you can throw anything more out the window!
The notes to the song are below. Write the words of
another nursery rhyme to fit the music.

Throw It Out the Window

Nursery Rhyme Parody

out the win - dow, the

win - dow, the sec-ond sto-ry win - dow.

Name That Pitch

The first two lines of music are from the song "Cumberland Gap." The second two lines are from the song "En roulant ma boule." Find *do* for each song. Then figure out the pitches of the other notes. Write each pitch name below the note.

Cumberland Gap

En roulant ma boule

Mid-Unit Review

Write the answers to these riddles. Use words from the lessons.
Write one letter in each blank.

1. A group of words can make a thought
That's able to amaze.
A group of notes that make a thought
Is called a musical __ __ __ __ __ __.

2. I give the following advice:
Play it once; play it twice.

__ __ __ __ __ __   __ __ __ __

3. You sing me over and over again.
I hope it's not a pain.
You might call me a *chorus,*
Or just a sweet __ __ __ __ __ __ __

4. A pitch two notes below *do* —ta-da!
You can just call me __ __ __   __ __

5. You play a __ __ __ __ __   __ __ __ __ __ __
And then they ask for more.
After the __ __ __ __ __ __   __ __ __ __ __ __
They're quickly out the door.

6. Ten of these would make a song
Quite lengthy to rehearse.
Remember, though, that each one is
A differently worded __ __ __ __ __.

7. A valley may be so low,
But a pitch can be __ __ __   __ __.

Samba!

Mambo, rumba, cha-cha, samba, tango—maybe you've heard of some of these Latin American dances. They all call up images of colorfully dressed couples dancing to music with lively rhythms. Of these dances, the samba is the one that comes from Brazil.

There are several ways the samba can be played and danced. During Brazil's Carnival celebration, the samba is danced very quickly and gaily. But the slower bossa nova, which became popular in the 1960s, is also a form of samba.

The samba has a long history that began when settlers from Portugal brought the first slaves from Africa. *Samba* means "to pray" in the religion that developed among the slaves. The music and dances of the slaves' religion became popular among all the people of Brazil. The samba went through many different forms over the centuries. It became well known in the United States from musical films in the 1930s and 1940s.

Do you want to learn the samba? Which kind?
You can find dance steps in books. You can probably find samba music in your library.

For now, take a blank sheet of paper and copy a map of Brazil. Show the cities of Rio de Janeiro, Brasilia, and São Paulo, as well as the Amazon River. Decorate your map with things related to Brazil, such as samba dancers, coffee beans, and sugarcane.

These Fish Have Notes

Pick one pattern from each group of fish. (A group is three fish with the same background. Look on both pages.) Cut out your patterns. Paste them on a separate sheet of paper in the order shown below. Then sing your three-fish pattern.

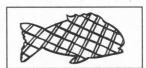

These Fish Have Notes

Spotlight Your Success! RESOURCE MASTER 3•11

Review

Circle the correct answer.

1. Compare these two phrases from "Cumberland Gap."
Choose the answer that best describes the two phrases.

a. same length, same rhythm, different pitches

b. same length, different rhythm, different pitches

c. different length, different rhythm, different pitches

2. Which song has low *so* and low *la* in it?

a. "Butterfly, Come Play with Me"

b. "Gi'Me Elbow Room"

c. "Lukey's Boat"

3. Which one of these patterns is a conducting pattern?

a.

b.

c. ostinato

Spotlight Your Success! RESOURCE MASTER 3•11

Read and Listen
Circle the correct answer.

1. Which rhythm do you hear?

a.

c.

b.

d.

Think
Write your answers. Use your own paper.

1. How is a musical phrase in a song like a sentence in a paragraph?

2. How can you tell when one phrase ends and a new one starts?

3. What does a repeat sign mean?

Create and Perform

Describe something you learned about the music from different countries.

_____

_____

Choose one song or dance to perform again. Write how would you teach that song or dance to someone else. List the steps in the order that you would perform them. Use your own paper.

Self-Assessment

Who worked with you on the unit project? Write everyone's name.

_____   _____

_____   _____

What did you like best about the project? _____

_____

What did you like least? _____

_____

If you could do the project again, what would you change? _____

_____

How did your group do during the performance?
The goals for the project are listed below.
Put an X in the box that shows how you did.

Goal	😁	🙂	😐	☹️
Our lyrics matched the rhythm of the tune.				
We sang together with a good tone.				
We kept the audience interested in our performance.				

Name _____ Date _____

Teacher Assessment

	Lyrics/Rhythm	Unison Singing	Stage Presence
Excellent	Lyrics matched the rhythm of the melody exactly.	Sang precisely in unison with a pleasing tone throughout.	Performed with a great deal of energy, focus, and confidence.
*Competent	Almost all the lyrics matched the rhythm of the melody.	Sang in unison with a pleasing tone through most of the performance.	Performed with a noticeable amount of energy, focus, and confidence.
Progressing	Some of the lyrics matched the rhythm of the melody.	Sang in unison, but occasionally one or two individual voices could be heard.	Performed with some amount of energy, focus, and confidence.
Showing Little Progress	Few of the lyrics matched the rhythm of the melody.	Sang in unison, but many divergent voices could be heard.	Performed with little energy, focus, and/or confidence.

Not Scorable: Did not participate.

*Competent is the expected level for all students.

School-to-Home Letter

Dear Family,

The United States is a country on the move, and it has the music to prove it. There are hundreds of songs about traveling, picking up stakes, settling elsewhere, and just roaming the countryside. We yearn for new and wonderful places while being nostalgic about home. In this unit your student will learn a number of songs that have to do with going places.

Your student will continue to learn about phrases, those groups of notes that make a musical thought. Some phrases in a song are identical, some are similar, and some are different. Rhythms, too, can be the same or different. In a song, they may provide a musical "question" and "answer."

In this unit your student will begin to see how simple songs can be made more elaborate. Many melodies vary beats within their rhythms and change pitches often. Some songs also have a secondary melody, or *ostinato,* a short phrase that repeats over and over. A good ostinato will create harmony, that pleasing combination of notes.

Your child will enjoy writing his or her own words to fit the beat of a familiar song. In this unit he or she will encounter sixteenth notes. These can provide four sounds to a single beat, depending on the rhythm of a song.

The concept of pitch becomes broader in this unit, with an exploration of pitches that repeat, step, or leap. The pentatonic, or five-toned, scale is also introduced.

Finally, your child starts to become familiar with the rondo, or canon, a song with five sections in the form A B A C A. Then, after traveling the world, all roads lead to home!

Sincerely,

Third Grade Music Teacher

School-to-Home Letter

Estimada Familia:

Estados Unidos es un país en marcha y tiene música con qué probarlo. Hay cientos de canciones sobre el tema de los viajes, emprender aventuras, establecerse en otro lugar y conducir por la carretera sin rumbo fijo. Deseamos lugares nuevos y maravillosos y a la vez tenemos nostalgia por nuestros hogares. En esta unidad su hijo aprenderá una cantidad de canciones que tienen que ver con los viajes.

Su hijo continuará aprendiendo el fraseo, el tipo de notas que componen un pensamiento musical. Algunos fraseos en una canción son idénticos, algunos son similares y algunos son diferentes. De la misma manera, los ritmos pueden ser iguales o diferentes. En una canción, pueden dar una "pregunta" y una "respuesta" musicales.

En esta unidad su hijo comenzará a notar cómo las canciones simples pueden convertirse en canciones más elaboradas. Muchas melodías varían los compases dentro de sus ritmos y cambian a menudo sus tonos. Algunas canciones también tienen una melodía, u *ostinato,* es decir un fraseo corto que se repite una y otra vez. Un buen *ostinato* creará armonía que es esa combinación agradable de notas.

Su hijo disfrutará escribiendo sus propias palabras para que entren dentro de los compases de una canción conocida. En esta unidad su hijo se encontrará con las semicorcheas. Estas pueden ofrecer cuatro sonidos para un único compás de tono, dependiendo del ritmo de la canción.

El concepto de tono (agudos) se profundiza en esta unidad, con una explicación sobre los tonos que se repiten, pasan o saltan. También se presenta la escala pentatónica, o de cinco notas.

Por último, su hijo o hija comienza a familiarizarse con el rondó o canon, una canción con cinco secciones con el esquema A B A C A. Y luego de haber recorrido todo el mundo, ¡todos los caminos conducen al hogar!

Atentamente,
Maestra de Música de Tercer Grado

Name _____ Date _____

Creative Unit Project

RESOURCE MASTER 4•2

For your Unit 4 project, your group will create a rondo form (ABACA). You will use movement and body percussion. Follow these steps.

STEP 1 (after Lesson 2)
• Review "Spinning Song." Do you remember the movements you learned? As a group, practice the movements. This will be the A section of your rondo.
• Now create your own 16-beat movement ostinato. It should have the same number of identical and similar phrases as "Spinning Song." Work together until you like the movements. This will be the B section of your rondo.

STEP 2 (after Lesson 3)
Review your 16-beat movement ostinato. Practice it. Then put it together with the A section (movements from "Spinning Song"). Practice the two parts as an ABA form. Really think as you practice. Are you sure that your A and B sections have the same number of identical and similar phrases? Make changes to your B section if you need to.

STEP 3 (after Lesson 4)
Now create a two-phrase body percussion ostinato. This will be the C section of your rondo form. Here are the guidelines.
• Include identical and similar phrases.
• Use a rhythm with four sounds to a beat.
Notate your ostinato on the next page.

Creative Unit Project

STEP 4 (after Lesson 8)

Review the pieces of your rondo.

A: Movement of "Spinning Song"

B: Your 16-beat movement ostinato

C: Your two-phrase body percussion ostinato

Remember that they go together in the form ABACA.

Practice until all the parts flow smoothly together.

Name _____ Date _____

Alike or Not?

Look at the first verse of "Stevedore's Song" in your textbook.

Sing and tap the rhythm of each of these pairs of phrases from the song. Then draw a line to the word that describes them. One word will be used two times.

• Phrases 1 and 2

• Phrases 3 and 4   identical

• Phrases 2 and 4   similar

• Phrases 1 and 3   different

Don't Lose That Beat   RESOURCE MASTER 4•5

The music below is for the song "Polly Wolly Doodle." Most of the words have been taken out. First, look at the version of the song in your music book. Notice the first verse with all the words. Then, replace the missing words in the music below with lyrics of your own. Will your song be about a girl or a boy? Where are you going? What will you be singing?

Polly Wolly Doodle

Southern American

1. Oh, I went _____ sing-ing

_____ My __ _____

Fare thee well,   fare thee well,   fare thee

well, my _____ for I'm goin' to _____ for to

see my _____ sing-ing _____

USE WITH GRADE 3, UNIT 4, LESSON 2

Name _____ Date _____

Quarter, Eighth, Sixteenth

1. Cut out the patterns to make flashcards.

2. Work in pairs. Clap one pattern. Did your partner guess the pattern? Take turns until you both have clapped out all the patterns.

Penta Means "Five"

Look at the music to the song "Shalom Chaveyrim." Write the pitch names under each of the notes. Then circle the pitches that are not part of the pentatonic scale. Rewrite the three measures that have those pitches. Use only pentatonic pitches so that the melody becomes pentatonic.

Shalom Chaveyrim
(Shalom, My Friends)

Israeli Folk Song

so, la, ti, do re mi fa so la ti do

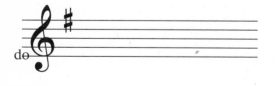 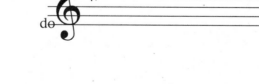

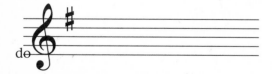

Mid-Unit Review

RESOURCE MASTER 4•8

Use the words in the box to complete this musical tale.

canon	pentatonic	sixteenth
high do	round	notes
identical	scale	unison
ostinato	similar	

I wanted to write a _____ song. I included the pitches *do, re,*

mi, so, la, and _____. If you play these in order, they make

a _____.

I wanted several of the measures of my song to be exactly the same,

or _____. I wanted several more measures to be _____,

or somewhat alike.

I couldn't decide whether I wanted to create a(n) _____ to go

with the main melody or whether I would rather write the song as a

_____, or _____. I didn't want a group of singers to

be singing in _____ at any point in the song. That would be

too boring!

Finally, I had to think of the rhythm. I knew that I wanted quarter,

eighth, and _____ notes. But I couldn't decide whether I

wanted any half or whole notes. That would be too slow!

Well, I guess I'd better start writing my song!

Repeated Notes, Steps, and Skips

Here is the music for "Jasmine Flower." On the line below the staff, and between each two notes, write:

- **R** for *Repeat* if the notes are on the same pitch;
- **ST** for *Step* if the note has moved one pitch up or down;
- **SK** for *Skip* if the note has moved more than one pitch up or down.

Jasmine Flower

Chinese Folk Song
Collected and Transcribed by Kathy Sorensen

A Musical Conversation

1. Clap this rhythmic question.

2. Write your own rhythmic answer by using these rhythms. Each box is one measure long.

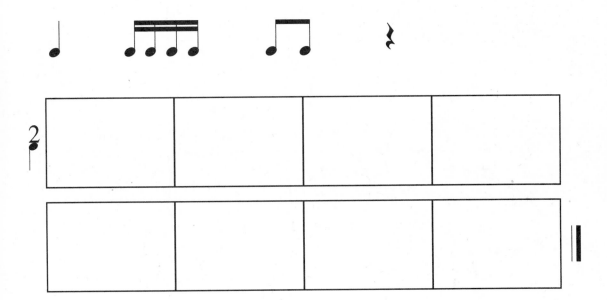

3. Now clap the question, and have a friend clap your answer.

Rondo on the Road

RESOURCE MASTER 4•11

Look at the following pictures of vehicles. Color each one, and then cut each out along the dotted lines. Finally, arrange them so that they are in rondo form.

USE WITH GRADE 3, UNIT 4, LESSON 8

Spotlight Your Success! RESOURCE MASTER 4•12

Review

Circle the correct answer.

1. Which song has high *do* in it?
   - a. Riding in a Buggy
   - b. J'entend le moulin
   - c. Dinah

2. Which pair of phrases below can be called similar?

   a.

   b.

   c.

3. How does a short musical phrase become an *ostinato*?
   - a. The musical phrase stops and starts.
   - b. The musical phrase repeats without changing.
   - c. The musical phrase is heard only during the second verse.

Read and Learn

Circle the correct answer.

1. Which rhythm do you hear?

   a.    c.

   b.    d.

Spotlight Your Success! RESOURCE MASTER 4•12

2. All of these pitch patterns begin on *so*. Which pattern do you hear?

a.

b.

c.

Think!
Write your answers. Use your own paper.

1. How can you tell if a musical piece is a rondo?

2. When you look at a melody on the staff, how can you tell leaps from steps?

3. Write about the two canons you sang in this unit. What makes these songs canons?

Create and Perform

Create rhythmic answers for the following rhythmic questions.
Form two groups to clap. Perform the questions and answers.

Name _____ Date _____

Self-Assessment

Who worked with you on the unit project? Write everyone's name.

_____   _____

_____   _____

What did you like best about the project? _____

_____

What did you like least? _____

_____

If you could do the project again, what would you change? _____

_____

How did your group do during the performance?
The goals for the project are listed below.
Put an X in the box that shows how you did.

Goal				
We moved smoothly between the parts of our rondo.				
We played the rhythm correctly and with energy.				
Our phrasing was clear.				

Name _____ Date _____

Teacher Assessment

RESOURCE MASTER 4•14

	Rondo Form and Transitions	**Phrasing**	**Rhythm**
Excellent	All sections were clearly distinct to the listener with smooth transitions from one section to another.	Sensitive to phrasing throughout the performance.	Consistently performed the rhythm with accuracy and a lot of confidence.
***Competent**	Almost all sections were clearly distinct to the listener with mostly smooth transitions from one section to another.	Sensitive to phrasing through most of the performance.	Performed the rhythm with accuracy and a good deal of confidence.
Progressing	Most sections were distinct to the listener with some smooth transitions from one section to another.	Sensitive to phrasing during some of the performance.	Generally performed the rhythm accurately, but occasional errors limited confidence.
Showing Little Progress	Some sections were distinct to the listener, and a few transitions were smooth.	Occasionally sensitive to phrasing during the performance.	Sporadically performed the rhythm accurately and with little evidence of confidence.

Not Scorable: Did not participate.

*Competent is the expected level for all students.

School-to-Home Letter

Dear Family,

In Unit 5 your child will focus on rhythm as she or he continues learning about the world of music. Your child will learn how beats are sometimes grouped in threes (as in OOM-pah-pah). Examples of songs in which the beats are grouped in threes are waltzes, "Clementine," and "Take Me Out to the Ball Game." However, melody and harmony are not neglected in this unit. Students will learn how to find the notes B, A, and G on the staff and identify the treble clef. Toward the end of the unit, students will begin to study chords and harmony, learning what happens when three or more notes are sounded at the same time.

The composers Wolfgang Amadeus Mozart and Johann Sebastian Bach will be introduced. Students will also learn about the Maori people of New Zealand and find out what a conductor does. They will learn a bit about bagpipes.

Sharing these musical experiences with your child will enhance his or her learning. Remember to listen to music, sing, and even dance with your child. It will be fun and enrich your time together.

Sincerely,

Third Grade Music Teacher

Nombre: _____ Fecha: _____

School-to-Home Letter

Estimada Familia:

En la unidad 5 su hijo se concentrará en el ritmo a medida que continúe aprendiendo sobre el mundo de la música. Su hijo aprenderá cómo a veces los compases se agrupan de a tres (como en el caso de UM-pa-pa). Los valses *"Clementine,"* y *"Take Me Out to the Ball Game"* son un ejemplo de canciones en las que los compases se agrupan de a tres. Sin embargo, la melodía y la armonía no quedan descuidadas en esta unidad. Los alumnos aprenderán cómo encontrar las notas B, A, y G en el pentagrama y cómo identificar la clave de sol. Hacia el final de la unidad, los alumnos comenzarán a estudiar los acordes y la armonía, aprendiendo qué ocurre cuando tres o más notas suenan al mismo tiempo.

Se presentará a los compositores Wolfgang Amadeus Mozart y Johann Sebastian Bach. Los alumnos también aprenderán sobre los maoríes de Nueva Zelanda y descubrirán qué hace un director de orquesta. Aprenderán algo sobre las gaitas.

El hecho de compartir estas experiencias musicales con su hijo mejorará su aprendizaje. Recuerde escuchar música, cantar e incluso bailar con su hijo o hija. Será divertido y enriquecerá el tiempo que pasen juntos.

Atentamente,

Maestra de Música de Tercer Grado

Name _____ Date _____

Creative Unit Project

RESOURCE MASTER 5•2

Your Unit 5 project is to create a machine! If it were real, your machine would do a daily chore for you. You and your group will dream up a machine and create rhythms to go along with it. You will draw a picture of the machine. Then you will perform the rhythm and movements that go with it. Follow these steps.

STEP 1 (after Lesson 1)
What is your machine? What can it do for you? Think of ideas. Choose your favorite. Name the machine.

_____

How does the machine work? Create an eight-beat rhythm to show its work. Use the notes ♩, ♫, and 𝅝

Write your rhythm below.

Show your rhythm using mouth sounds like tongue clicks or other noises (*Zzzz! Psst! Shhh!*). You might also use body percussion and movements. Make the rhythm show what your machine can do. This eight-beat rhythm is the A part of your performance piece.

STEP 2 (after Lesson 2)

Now create the B part of your piece. This time, create a six-beat rhythm pattern. Use the notes ♩, ♫, and ♩ (half note)

Write your rhythm on the next page.

Creative Unit Project

RESOURCE MASTER

Again, show your rhythm using mouth sounds, body percussion, and movements. Then put the A and B parts together. Practice your AB piece.

STEP 3 (after Lesson 3)

Have each member of your group write a description of your machine. What does it do? How does it work? Share your descriptions. Choose your favorite one. Together, work on the writing until it is just right.

Now practice your A and B rhythm patterns again. This time, put them together in ABA form. Remember to keep the rhythm at a steady tempo throughout.

How can you improve your performance? Here are some ideas.

• Change the length of the A or B section. For example, repeat one of the ostinatos to make a section longer.
• Change how loud or soft the sections are.
• Move the way you think the machine might move.

Keep practicing until the group is ready to have your teacher record your piece.

STEP 4 (after Lesson 8)

Have each member of your group draw a picture of your machine. Share the drawings. Choose your favorite one. You might put two or more drawings together.

Listen to the recording your teacher made of your piece. Improvise movements to do along with the recording. Practice these movements until you are ready for the final performance!

Name _____ Date _____

Think in Threes

1. Clap these rhythms that have three beats to the measure.

a.

b.

c.

2. Draw the bar lines so that each measure has three beats.

a.

b.

c.

3. Fill in the measures with half notes (𝅗𝅥), quarter notes (♩), two

   eighth notes (♫), or quarter rests (𝄽) so that each measure has

   three beats.

a.

b.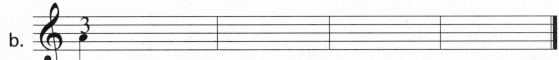

Repeated Rhythms

RESOURCE MASTER 5•5

1. Write a rhythm ostinato for the song "Boll Weevil." Use these notes and rests to create your rhythm: ♩, 𝄾, ♫, and 𝅗𝅥 Your ostinato should have the same number of beats per measure as "Boll Weevil" and should repeat several times during the song. Remember to put stress on the downbeats.

2. What rhythm instruments would you use to play your "Boll Weevil" ostinato? Why? _____

_____

3. Write a rhythm ostinato for the song "Bella bimba." Use these notes and rests to create your rhythm: ♩, 𝄾, ♫, and 𝅗𝅥 Your ostinato should have the same number of beats per measure as "Bella bimba" and should repeat several times during the song. Remember to put stress on the downbeats.

4. What rhythm instruments would you use to play your "Bella bimba" ostinato? Why? _____

_____

The Maori People

Read about the Maori people. Then answer the questions below.

The Maori people have lived in New Zealand for about 800 years. New Zealand is in the southern Pacific Ocean near Australia. The Maori call New Zealand *Aotearoa,* which means "land of the long white cloud." They came to New Zealand from other islands in the South Pacific. The language that they spoke is like the language spoken by Hawaii's native people. Hawaii is also in the South Pacific. Only about one quarter of Maoris still speak this language. Most of them now speak English.

The arts have always been very important to the Maori people. Maoris make music, write poetry, speak in public, or make carvings. These carvings are used to decorate buildings or might be made into jewelry.

The Maori use a different calendar than we do. Their year begins after the first new moon in June, instead of in January as ours does.

1. Where is New Zealand? _____

   _____

2. What language is closely related to the Maori language?

   _____

3. What art form is used to decorate Maori buildings?

   _____

4. When does the Maori year begin? _____

   _____

Name _____ Date _____

The Conductor's Job

Read about what conductors do. Then answer the questions below.

Conductors are people who stand in front of a band or an orchestra and move their hands in time to the music so that the musicians stay together while they are playing. Conductors may use a stick called a baton, or they may conduct with only their hands.

Conductors do much more than just keep time, however. They often choose the music that the band or orchestra will play. They also spend a lot of time rehearsing and teaching the musicians to play the music in a certain way.

Most conductors are highly educated. They go to special colleges called conservatories to learn about music and to learn how to be a good conductor. Only the best ones will get jobs with large orchestras.

One famous conductor was Leopold Stokowski. He led the Philadelphia Orchestra from 1912 to 1947. He is famous for shaking Mickey Mouse's hand before conducting the orchestra in the Walt Disney film *Fantasia.*

Leonard Bernstein was the conductor of the New York Philharmonic from 1958 to 1969. He thought that it was very important for students to learn about classical music, so he held special concerts just for kids. They were often shown on television.

1. What is the name of the stick conductors use? _____

2. What else do conductors do besides keep time? _____

    _____

3. What special colleges do conductors often attend?

    _____

4. Why did Leonard Bernstein conduct special concerts for students?

    _____

Name _____ Date _____

Mid-Unit Review

RESOURCE MASTER

1. For how many beats do these notes, groups of notes, or rests last?

_____ a. 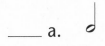 _____ b.   _____ c.

_____ d.   _____ e.   _____ f.

2. Decide which of these rhythms are in $\frac{3}{4}$ meter and which are in $\frac{4}{4}$ meter. Write the answer in the blank.

_____ a.

_____ b.

_____ c.

3. Draw bar lines so that this rhythm is in $\frac{4}{4}$ meter.

4. Draw bar lines so that this rhythm is in $\frac{3}{4}$ meter.

5. Does this rhythm begin on an upbeat or a downbeat? _____

USE WITH GRADE 3, UNIT 5, MID-UNIT REVIEW

Melodic Ostinato

1. Create your own rhythmic ostinato for "Night Song."

Use: 𝄽, ♩, ♩, and ♩.

2. Use your ostinato to write a melody.

Choose pitches from the G chord, and assign one pitch to each note.

G chord   G   B   D

3. Perform your melody as an ostinato accompaniment to "Night Song."

The Shepherd and His Sheep

RESOURCE MASTER 5•10

Find out what happened to this shepherd by writing either G, A, or B in the blanks.

G   A   B

A shepherd in the Scottish Hi__hl__nds pl__yed

his _ _ _ pipes for his l __ m __ s. The l __ m __ s

l __u __hed, __i __ __led, __nd __ __ __ __ ed __ ec __ use

they were __ l __ d to he __ r the __ __ __ pipe music.

One d __ y, the shepherd's __ __ __ pipes __ roke. The

l__ m __ s so __ __ ed __nd __ ro __ ned. The shepherd

tr __velled to the city __nd __ou __ht new __ __ __ pipes.

Around and Around

Read about circle dances around the world.
Then answer the questions below.

"Let's Go Dancing" is a circle dance. A group of people form a circle and perform certain movements. Circle dances are done all over the world. In many cultures, they are a symbol of community unity.

The gavotte was started in France about 500 years ago. Couples perform lively skipping steps to music that has two beats in each measure. In early forms of the gavotte, one couple would leave the circle and kiss all of the other dancers.

In Korea, during the Harvest Moon Festival in the fall, women perform the *kanggangsuwollae* dance. The name means "watch the surroundings." The dancers form a circle around a singer, who sings about happiness, long life, and love. The dancers start moving very slowly, but they gradually speed up. By the end of the dance, they are moving very quickly.

Young women in India perform a circle dance called the tiruvathira. Each woman claps her hands against the hands of the women on either side of her as they all move around in a circle. While they are dancing, the women also sing a song that tells a story.

1. What do circle dances symbolize in many cultures? _____

_____

2. Where was the gavotte first performed? _____

3. When do people perform the kanggangsuwollae? _____

_____

4. What do tiruvathira dancers do while they move in a circle?

_____

Spotlight Your Success! RESOURCE MASTER 5•12

Review
Circle the correct answer.

1. Which one of these melodies starts on a downbeat?

a.

b.

c.

Read and Listen
Circle the correct answer.

1. Which rhythm do you hear?

2. Which rhythm do you hear?

Spotlight Your Success! RESOURCE MASTER

3. Which rhythm do you hear?

a. $\frac{3}{4}$ ♩ ♩ ♩ | ♩. ‖   c. $\frac{3}{4}$ ♩. | ♩ ♩ 𝄾 ‖

b. $\frac{3}{4}$ ♩ ♩ ♩ | ♫ ♫ ♩ ‖

Think!
Write your answer. Use your own paper.

1. Can one recorder play a chord? Can one guitar? Explain why.

2. How can you tell if the song you are listening to has beat groupings of three or four?

3. Describe one way to create harmony to accompany a melody.

4. Which of these instruments can play a whole note—woodblock or triangle? Explain why.

5. Write about what the conductor's arm movement pattern show the orchestra besides the tempo. How does this help the orchestra play well together?

Create and Perform

Create a 4-measure ostinato for "Bella bimba." Write it on the rhythm line below.

Perform it for the class, while the teacher plays "Bella bimba" on an instrument.

Name _____ Date _____

Self-Assessment

Who worked with you on the unit project? Write everyone's name.
Tell the best thing each person did for the project.

_____

_____

_____

What did you like best about the project? _____

_____

What did you like least? _____

_____

If you could do the project again, what would you change? _____

_____

How did your group do during the performance?
The three goals for the project are listed below.
Put an X in the box that shows how you did.

Goal	😁	🙂	😐	🙁
We all helped with the project.				
We had good ideas for our machine movements and sound, and they helped our performance.				
We stayed together with a steady tempo.				

Name _____ Date _____

Teacher Assessment

RESOURCE MASTER 5•14

	Steady Tempo	Group Participation	Creative Choices
Excellent	Consistently performed with a steady tempo throughout.	All students participated and contributed to the project throughout.	Creative choices for machine and sounds were innovative and enhanced the overall effect of the performance.
*Competent	Performed with a steady tempo almost all of the time.	Most students participated and contributed to the project.	Creative choices for machine and sounds were unique and added to the overall effect of the performance.
Progressing	Performed with a steady tempo most of the time, but with a few noticeable lapses.	Some students participated and contributed to the project.	Some creative choices for machine and sounds were unusual, but did not contribute positively to the overall effect of the performance.
Showing Little Progress	Performed with a steady tempo part of the time, but with many obvious lapses.	Very few students participated and contributed to the project.	A few creative choices for machine and sounds were unusual, but they detracted from the overall effect of the performance.

Not Scorable: Did not participate.

*Competent is the expected level for all students.

Optional: A secret ballot may be used to choose the winning concept. Students should decide their vote based on the creativity of the concept, the quality of the illustration, and performance skills. The winning illustration may be posted in the school hall.

Name _____ Date _____

School-to-Home Letter

Dear Family,

The last unit of our music curriculum will acquaint your student with many new musical terms and concepts. First, students will discover that melodies have a "tonal center," a home base note that anchors the tune. The melody usually returns to this center at its end. Students will learn how to identify the tonal center in songs that are written in both major and minor keys.

Some of the elements that make music expressive will be introduced. Often music does not have a steady beat. When a part of a piece speeds up, the movement is called *accelerando.* Notes may also be played in different ways. They can be smooth and connected (*legato*), or they can played in a short and choppy manner (*staccato*). Your student will learn how musicians create these different effects on stringed instruments by either using their bows or plucking the strings.

This unit will introduce the concept of dividing music into sections and phrases while reinforcing the musical elements of rhythm and meter presented earlier. In addition, students will learn the words for numbers and months in Spanish and a little about reggae music, Brazilian folk music, Mexican dance, and limericks. They will also meet the Russian composer Sergei Prokofiev.

By participating in your student's musical learning, you will demonstrate that you appreciate the importance of music in your life. Sing and dance with your student at home, and encourage him or her to create melodies, rhythms, and dance steps. You will both be glad that you did.

Sincerely,

Third Grade Music Teacher

School-to-Home Letter

Estimada Familia:

La última unidad de nuestro programa musical familiarizará a su hijo con muchos términos y conceptos musicales nuevos. Primero, los alumnos descubrirán que las melodías tienen un "centro tonal", una nota tónica central que fija la tonada. La melodía generalmente vuelve a su centro al finalizar. Los alumnos aprenderán a identificar el centro tonal en canciones escritas en escalas mayor y menor.

Se presentarán algunos de los elementos que hacen que la música sea expresiva. Con frecuencia la música no tiene un compás (de tono) continuo. Cuando una parte de la pieza se acelera, el movimiento se llama *accelerando.* Además, las notas pueden tocarse de diferentes maneras. Pueden ser suaves y sucesivas (*legato*), o pueden tocarse de un modo corto y picado (*staccato*). Su hijo aprenderá el modo en que los músicos crean diferentes efectos en instrumentos de cuerda usando sus arcos o punteando las cuerdas.

Esta unidad también presentará el concepto de la división musical en secciones y fraseos mientras se refuerzan los elementos musicales de ritmo y métrica previamente presentados. Además los alumnos aprenderán los números y los meses en español y un poquito de música *reggae,* música folklórica brasilera, bailes mexicanos y quintillas jocosas (*limericks*). Conocerán además al compositor ruso Sergei Prokofiev.

Al participar en el aprendizaje musical de su hijo usted demuestra que valora la importancia de la música en su vida. Cante y baile con su hijo o hija en casa dándole aliento para que cree melodías, ritmos y pasos de baile. Los dos estarán felices de haberlo hecho.

Atentamente,

Maestra de Música de Tercer Grado

Creative Unit Project

RESOURCE MASTER 6•2

Your Unit 6 project is to create and perform a piece with several sections. You will get to sing, play drums and pitched instruments, and use body percussion. Follow the steps below.

STEP 1 (after Lesson 1)
Practice singing "The Ballad of the Bedbugs and the Beetles."
• The first time through, everyone sings.
• The second time through, have one group member play a steady beat on a drum.
• Sing the song again. This time, have one person drum a steady beat. Have everyone else create body percussion to match the rhythm of the words.
• Practice the song a final time. This time, have the drummer play eight beats as an introduction. Then everyone should join in to sing and play the body percussion.
This final way of singing the song is the A section of your piece.

STEP 2 (after Lesson 3)
Practice singing "Charlie."
• The first time through, everyone sings. Practice blending your voices.
• Have one group member play a steady beat on a drum.
• Sing the song again. This time, have someone play an eight-beat introduction on the xylophone. Then everyone should join in to sing and create body percussion to match the rhythm of the words.
This song is the B section of your piece.

Creative Unit Project

STEP 3 (after Lesson 8)

Now put your piece together. Here is the order of the parts:

    1) eight-beat drum introduction

    2) Section A: "The Ballad of the Bedbugs and the Beetles" (sung and performed with body percussion)

    3) eight-beat xylophone interlude

    4) Section B: "Charlie" (sung and performed with body percussion)

Practice the piece. Work on blending your voices, keeping a steady beat, and staying together. Make sure that you are moving in tempo from part to part. After each time through, ask yourselves how you are doing. Make changes as needed. Keep practicing until you are ready to perform.

Rounding the Bases

RESOURCE MASTER 6•4

Use the notes from the G pentatonic scale to create a melody for the rhythm above the staff. Draw in the notes for your melody on the staff below. The song should end on the home tone of G.

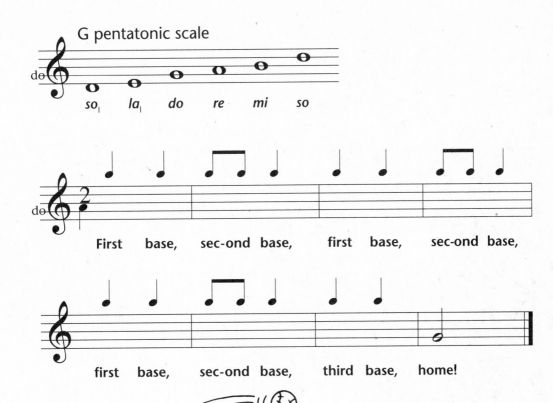

G pentatonic scale

do

so̗ la̗ do re mi so

do

First   base,   sec-ond base,   first   base,   sec-ond base,

first   base,   sec-ond base,   third base,   home!

Getting Centered

1. Here is the melody for the song "Uno de enero."
   Draw a circle around any beats that have three notes.
   Draw a square around the tonal center wherever you see it.

Uno de enero
(The First of January)

Mexican Folk Song

2. Create a two-measure rhythm ostinato to go with "Uno de enero."

Name _____ Date _____

Dancing with Props

Read about some dances that use props.
Then answer the questions below.

Many dances need more than just music and dancers. Sometimes the dancers hold things in their hands or dance around an object on the floor. Here are a few examples:

In Korea, groups of young women perform a fan dance for festivals celebrating birthdays or the seasons. They move very gracefully as they hold their fans. Their movements represent things in nature like flowers, butterflies, and rivers.

The Mexican Hat Dance is known as *jarabe tapatío* in Mexico. It is a dance for couples. The man throws his sombrero (a large Mexican hat) onto the floor, and the woman dances around it.

In Bali, an island in Indonesia, middle-aged men perform a dance called the Baris dance. The men play warriors and cover themselves in beads and flowers. They wear scarves that they say are magical. The warriors dance in two lines and often stop and stand like heroes in battle. Then the music becomes violent, and they act out a battle. Because the dance has many difficult moves and the dancers must make fierce faces, the dancers are very strong and flexible.

1. What do the movements in the Korean fan dance represent?

_____

2. Who performs the Baris dance? _____

_____

3. What do Baris dancers wear? _____

_____

Pitches and Centers

1. Look at the pieces of songs below. Label each note with pitch syllables (*do, re, mi, so,* and *la*).

2. Sing each example.

3. Draw a box around the tonal center in each example each time it appears.

a.

__ __ __ __ __ __ __ __ __ __

b.

__ __ __ __ __ __ __ __ __ __

c.

__ __ __ __ __ *ti* __ __ __ __ __

d.

__ __ __ __ __ __ __ __ __ __ __

Name _____ Date _____

Mid-Unit Review

Is each statement true or false? Write T or F in the blank provided. If a statement is false, rewrite it so that it is true.

____ 1. Melodies rarely begin on the pitch that is the tonal center, but they always end on the tonal center.

_____

____ 2. Three equal sounds to one beat is shown as

_____

____ 3. The Chiapas region of Mexico is along the U.S.–Mexico border.

_____

____ 4. "One More River" tells the story of the first steamships on the Mississippi.

_____

Follow the directions to identify the tonal center.

5. Here is the C major scale. Circle the tonal center.

6. Here is the G pentatonic scale. Circle the tonal center.

Speed It Up

1. Read the story below. Suppose that you are going to set these
   words to music. Put a slash (/) where you think an *accelerando*
   would begin.

Sandra had a baseball cap that she loved. She wore it

every day, and she did not want to take it off even

when it was time for bed. One day Sandra was riding her

bicycle down the street when a gust of wind blew her

cap right off her head! The wind blew harder and carried

her cap farther and farther away. Sandra pedaled her

bicycle faster and faster to try to catch her cap. She

rode down a hill and picked up even more speed. Just

when she thought that she could not go any faster and was

all out of breath, she found her cap caught in a bush.

2. Now write your own paragraph. Tell about something that goes
   faster and faster. Have a friend guess where the *accelerando* should
   start. Did he or she pick the same place that you did?

_____

_____

_____

_____

_____

_____

Make Your Marks

Alabama Bound

I'm Alabama bound,

I'm Alabama bound,

And if the train don't stop and turn around,

I'm Alabama bound.

1. Read the words of the American folk song "Alabama Bound."

2. Choose words to say *staccato* (•) or *legato* (⌒). Mark those words, and then say them out loud, following your markings.

3. Try saying the words at fast, medium, and slow tempos. Try starting slow and getting faster. Which tempo do you like best? Mark it above the words.

4. Mark the words with the dynamics you like best. Try loud (*f*), soft (*p*), or a combination of both.

5. Practice saying the words with all of the markings. Then perform your version for the class.

Rearranging Rhythms

1. Cut out the patterns below. Use four of them to make an eight-beat phrase. Use at least one pattern that has three sounds on a beat. End your phrase with a ♩. or 𝄽.

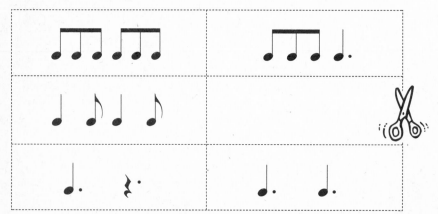

2. Use the space below to write your own limerick. It should have the same rhythm pattern as the one about the mouse on page 234 of your music book. Make sure that the first, second, and fifth lines rhyme. Use one of the phrases below as the first line of your limerick, or make up one of your own.

An old man who lived in a shoe . . .
A cat was caught up in a tree . . .
There was a young fish in a lake . . .
A jogger went out after dark . . .

_____

_____

_____

USE WITH GRADE 3, UNIT 6, LESSON 8

Spotlight Your Success! RESOURCE MASTER 6•11

Review

Circle the correct answer.

Identify the tonal center in each of the melodies below.

1.

   a. *do*   b. *la*

2.

   a. *do*   b. *la*

3.

   a. *do*   b. *la*

Name _____ Date _____

Spotlight Your Success! RESOURCE MASTER

Read and Listen   Circle the correct answer.

1. Listen to the drum play three different rhythm patterns, and decide whether you have heard three sounds on a beat in rhythm a, b, or c.

2. Identify the correct notation for the rhythm you hear.

Think!   Write your answers. Use your own paper.

1. Explain the meaning of the home tone in a melody.
2. Describe how you figure out if a song's tonal center is do or la.
3. Why do you think composers and performers use sudden and gradual changes in the tempo and dynamics of their music?
4. Write about how you would change your performance of a song if you see the words *staccato* or *legato* on the score.

Create and Perform

Create your own melody and rhythm over eight beats.

1. Use *so₁ la₁ do re me so la*.

2. Use $\overset{2}{\mathsf{f}}$ for your meter signature.

3. Use ♩♪, ♪♪♩, ♩., and ⁊ to create your rhythm pattern.

4. Decide whether your melody should end on the tonal center *do* or *la*.

Perform your melody for the class.

Name _____ Date _____

Self-Assessment

Who worked with you on the unit project? Write everyone's name.

_____   _____

_____   _____

What did you like best about the project? _____

_____

What did you like least? _____

_____

If you could do the project again, what would you change? _____

_____

How did your group do during the performance?
The goals for the project are listed below.
Put an X in the box that shows how you did.

Goal	😀	🙂	😐	🙁
Our voices blended together.				
We moved in tempo between the different sections.				
We sang and played at a steady tempo.				
Our group stayed together in rhythm while doing our different body percussion movements.				

Name _____ Date _____

Teacher Assessment

	Blend of Voices	Steady Tempo	Rhythm of the Words
Excellent	Voices blended together extremely well, and no individual voices could be heard.	Sang and played with a steady tempo throughout the performance with no difficulty.	Consistently played rhythm of the words accurately.
*Competent	Voices blended together well, so that rarely was an individual voice heard.	Sang and played with a steady tempo for most of the performance with little difficulty.	Played rhythm of the words accurately almost all of the performance.
Progressing	Voices generally blended together, but occasionally a few individual voices could be heard.	Sang and played with a steady tempo for part of the performance, but experienced some difficulty.	Played the rhythm of the words for most of the performance, but with some noticeable mistakes.
Showing Little Progress	Individual voices that did not blend with the others were frequently heard.	Sang and played with an unsteady tempo for most of the performance, and experienced a lot of difficulty.	Played the rhythm of the words for some of the performance, but with many noticeable mistakes.

Not Scorable: Did not participate.

*Competent is the expected level for all students.

Quarter and Eighth Notes

1. What are the hand signs for *mi, re,* and *do?* With a partner, practice making the hand signs while your partner sings the notes. Then switch roles so that both of you can practice singing the notes.

mi    *re*   *do*

2. Look in your textbook on page 242. How are the notes of the song "Rain Is Falling Down" like the title?

_____

3. Fill in the missing notes and rests. Then write the pitch names under the notes. Which notes are repeated? What goes in the measure with the single note? How does it sound?

mi mi re re do   __ __ __ __ __ __

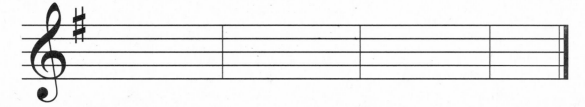

__ __ __ __ __ __ __ __ __ __

4. Tap the rhythms, and then sing the whole song.

Melodic Steps and Skips

1. Sing "Frog in the Meadow", on page 243 of your textbook, using *do, re,* and *mi.* Which notes stay on the same step? Which notes step down one at a time? Do any notes skip a step?

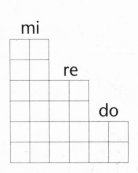

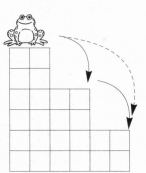

2. Copy the notes and rests of "Frog in the Meadow" in the blank measures below each example.

Frog in the mea-dow, Can't get him out!

Take a lit-tle stick and stir him a-bout!

Name _____ Date _____

Composing a Melody

Just like the composer, Ralph Vaughn Williams, you can use an everyday object as inspiration for composing your own melody!

Write the name of a kitchen utensil of your choice. _____

Is the utensil moved in straight lines or circles when it is used?

_____

How could a melody suggest straight lines? How about curved lines?

_____

Compose a melody with *do, re,* and *mi* on the staff below. Try to make it move to suggest either straight lines or curved lines, like your chosen utensil. Here are the three pitches to use.

There will be two beats in each measure. Use any two of the following in each measure:

Give your melody a title. Try playing your melody.

Composing with *So* and *La*

1. What are the hand signs for *so* and *la*?

so    *la*

2. Fill in the blank notes, and then sing the pentatonic (five-pitch) scale. Find those pitches in "Coral" on page 249 of your textbook.

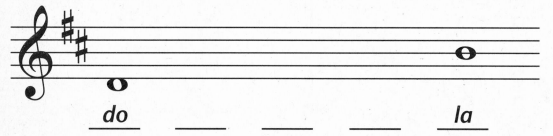

do ____   ____   ____   ____   la

3. Now write a composition that includes *so* and *la*. Use the rhythms above the staff to complete your work. End the composition on *so*. Add words, and sing it for the class.

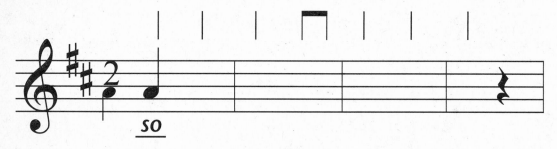

so

so

Improvising "Morning Music"

The following questions will help you and your group make decisions about creating an improvisation for "Morning Music" on page 251 of your textbook. When you have made your decisions and checked them with your teacher, you will be ready to improvise!

1. Who will begin improvising the melody on *do re mi so la?*
2. What will you use for an accompaniment for the melody?

Here are some ideas:
• A *tremolo* on any two pitches on lower-pitched instruments.
• Long sounds on C and G (*do* and *so*) on lower-pitched instruments.

3. Decide how you will suggest the sunrise.

Here are some ideas:
• Gradually add more melody and percussion instruments.
Write your decision. _____

4. How will you suggest sea sounds in an introduction?

Here are some ideas:
• Brush your fingernails on a textured drumhead.
• Lightly strum an autoharp.
• Play glissandi on barred instruments.
Write your decision. _____

5. How will people in your group know when to start and stop?
Will you have a conductor?

Write your decision. _____

Writing *Do Re Mi So La* RESOURCE MASTER (R•6)

Do can be on any line or space. When *do* changes, *re, mi, so,* and *la* change, too.

On each musical staff below, fill in *re, mi, so,* and *la* after the *do* already shown.

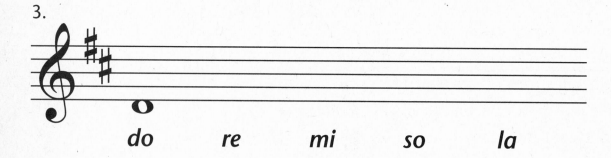

1.

do   re   mi   so   la

2.

do   re   mi   so   la

3.

do   re   mi   so   la

Play each of the pitches you wrote in 1, 2, and 3 above.

Find the Pitch

1. Fill in the names of the two mystery notes below.

<u>mi</u> <u>mi</u> <u>do</u> ___ ___ <u>do</u>

2. Add the missing notes, and sing them.

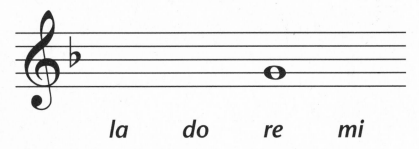

la   **do**   **re**   **mi**

3. Find low *la* in the song "Old Mr. Rabbit," and circle those notes.

<u>do</u>

4. Clap the rhythm of the whole song once, and then sing it using the words in your textbook on page 254.

Low La

1. Fill in the names of the notes in the blanks under "See the Rabbit Running," and then sing the pitches.

See the Rabbit Running

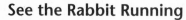

Hungarian Melody
Traditional English Words

mi mi mi re
See the rab- bit run - ning, from the fox who's cun - ning,

Fox is get - ting thin - ner, chas - ing down his din - ner.

2. Circle the lowest notes in the song.

3. If *do* is on the middle step, where is low *la*? Write it on the correct step.

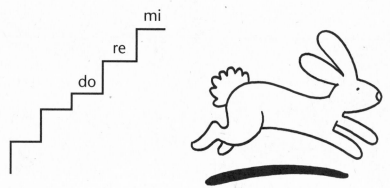

4. Now sing the words to "See the Rabbit Running."

Conducting in

1. Clap the rhythm in "Scotland's Burning." How many beats are there in each measure?

Scotland's Burning

Traditional Round

2. Stand up and clap the rhythm again. This time, stomp along with the beat, using two stomps for each measure. Follow your teacher conducting the song.

3. Take turns singing and conducting with a group of your classmates.

Writing Low So and La

1. Fill in the names of the notes, and sing this short excerpt from "Turn the Glasses Over," on page 260 of your textbook.

do

do ____ ____ ____ ____

2. Look through the verse, and see how many times you can find the same pattern. Find the measures that look the same, and write them below. Find the measures that look almost the same. Write them on the second staff below. How are they different?

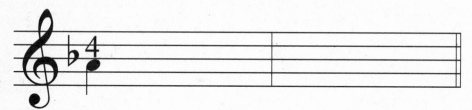

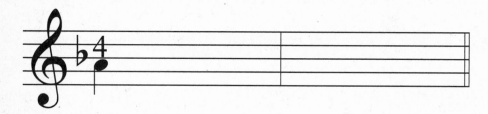

3. This song has two sections: the verse and the refrain. Circle the correct statement.

A. You can sing the refrain when you get tired of all the verses.

B. The words to the refrain change with every new verse.

C. You sing the refrain after every verse, but the words to the refrain always stay the same.

Composing a Melody in $\frac{2}{8}$

1. Suppose that you are on a farm where all the animals sing. Using the rhythm above the staff, write your own melody. Use *mi, re, do,* and write the pitch names underneath the notes. Remember, *do* is on the second line.

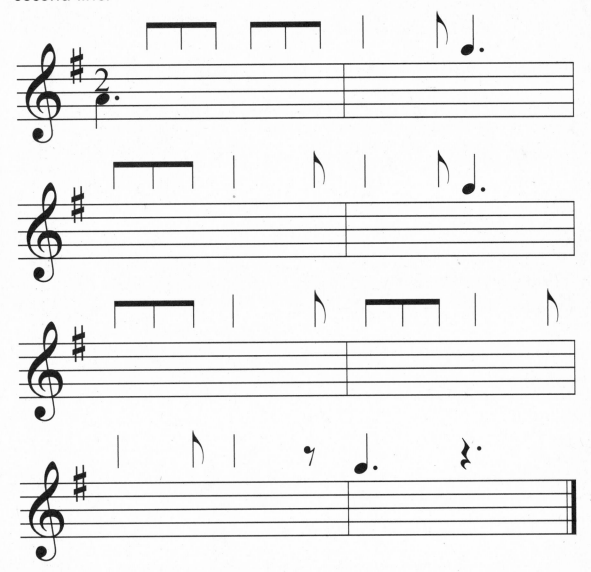

2. Make up words to your song, and sing it.

Sixteenth Notes

RESOURCE MASTER

1. Clap the rhythm to "Golden Ring Around the Susan Girl."

Golden Ring Around the Susan Girl

American Folk Song

Gold-en ring a-round the Su-san girl, Gold-en ring a-round the Su-san girl,

Gold-en ring a-round the Su-san girl, All the way a-round our Su-san girl.

2. How many sixteenth notes equal one beat in the song? Sing the words to the song, and notice how the words fit perfectly with the sixteenth notes.

3. Write your own melody with these pitches. Use quarter notes, eighth notes, and sixteenth notes in any combination as long as they add up to two beats per measure.

4. Make up words to your song, and sing it.

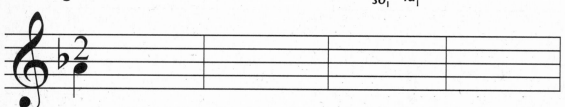

so₁ la₁ do re mi so

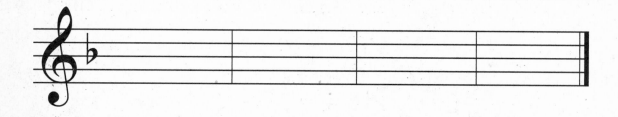

USE WITH GRADE 3, UNIT 4

Write the Missing *Do*

RESOURCE MASTER

Find the missing *do*s in "Circle 'Round the Zero," and write them on the staff. Then label the other notes in the song.

Remember: *Do* is in the first space below the staff. High *do* is on the fourth line of the staff.

High *Do*

1. Fill in the missing notes and names of the notes in the following music. Are they quarter notes, eighth notes, or sixteenth notes?

do do do do re re re re mi mi mi mi so

la la la la so so so so   mi re do re do

2. In the second to the last bar, how are the eighth-note pair and quarter note the same? How are they different?

3. Now sing the words to "One Potato, Two Potato," on page 267 of your textbook.

Name _____ Date _____

Writing High *Do*

1. Fill in the missing pitches in "Morning Bells," found on page 270 of your textbook.

2. Count the number of lines and spaces between *do* and high *do*. What is the distance between the two notes called? (Circle one)

    A. a rondo

    B. a fifth

    C. an octave

    D. a bridge

3. Now fill in the missing high *do* in each measure. Write high *do* in the blank.

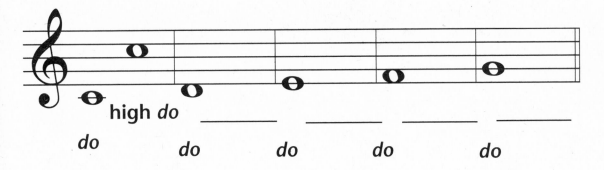

Find the Missing *Do*

1. Find missing *do* on each of the following staffs. If it is high *do*, write *do*. If it is *do,* write high *do*. Write it in as a quarter note.

2. Now write *do* after your high *do* or high *do* after your *do*. Write them as an eighth-note pair.

On the Upbeat

1. Look at the song "Smoke Goes Up the Chimney" in your textbook on page 272. Silently read the melody and "hear" the pitches. Both the first and the last measures have only half the number of beats they should have. What does this mean? Circle one.

    A. The composer didn't know math.

    B. The first bar and the last bar together make a full bar,
       so nothing is lost.

    C. The bar lines are in the wrong place.

2. To conduct an upbeat, raise your arms; for the downbeat, lower them. Working with a partner, sing the song while your partner conducts. Remember to begin the song by raising your arms in an upbeat.

3. Now, have one person sing "Smoke Goes Up the Chimney" while a partner claps the ostinato (a rhythm that is repeated over and over) below.

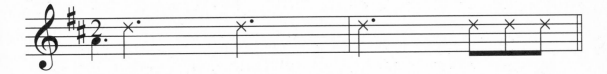

Whole Notes

1. Fill in the names of the notes in "Death of the Robin," and then sing the song, found on page 275 of your textbook.

Death of the Robin

Appalachian Folk Song

_mi_ _____ _____ _la_ _____
Who   killed   the___   Rob - in?

Who   killed   the___   Rob - in?

_la_ _____ _____ _____ _____
I,   cried the spar-row, with my   lit - tle bow and ar - row.

_____ _____ _____ _____ _____
It was   I,   Oh___ it   was   I.

2. Find the whole note. How many beats does it have? (Circle one.)

    A. 3

    B. 12

    C. 1 1/2

    D. 4

Dotted Half Notes

1. How many beats does a dotted half note have in the song "Little Tommy Tinker," found on page 277 of your textbook? (Circle one.)

   A. 4   B. 3   C. 1   D. $2\frac{1}{2}$

2. In any line or space below, write how many sixteenth notes, eighth notes, and quarter notes equal a dotted half note.

3. Sing "Little Tommy Tinker" with a partner. As you begin, have your partner wait until the third bar to begin. This is called singing in canon. Be sure to keep a steady tempo.

Playing an Ostinato

1. Look at page 279 in your book, and find the upbeats in "Dide."
Play the upbeats followed by a quarter note on your lap or a drum.

2. Look at this rhythm pattern. Play it on your lap or a drum.
Underline the strong beats. Circle the weak beats.

3. Play the bars above over and over. This is called an "ostinato."

4. With a partner, sing the song "Dide" while your partner drums or
claps the ostinato.

Bugle Calls

1. Circle the dotted half notes in "Taps." Sing the song.

Day   is   done,   gone   the   sun,

From   the   lake,   from   the   hills,   from   the   sky;

All   is   well,   safe - ly   rest,

God   is   nigh._____

2. How many beats are in the dotted half note? _____

3. Write three different combinations of notes or notes plus rests from "Taps" that equal a dotted half note.

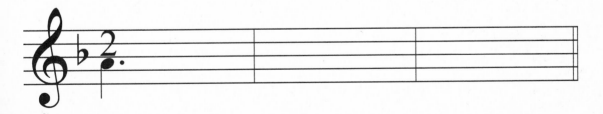

Compose and Improvise

Practice saying and clapping the following rhythms:

For ♩. - Say "web"

For ♩ ♪ - Say "spi-der"

For ♩♩♩ - Say "spin-ning a..."

1. ♩♪♩♪   2. ♩. ♩♩♩.   3. ♩. ♩.

4. ♩♩♩♩♩♩   5. ♩♪♪♪♪   6. ♩♩♩ ♩.

Use the rhythms to create two measures in meter below:

Fill in the pitch syllables for the notes below. Play your rhythm on these pitches on any barred instrument. Your new melodies can be interludes between verses of "Spiders," found on page 282 of your textbook.

C   D   F   G   A

do

A B A Form

Sing the following melody in A B A form, using the syllable "loo."

Section A

Section B

Section A

Answer these questions about the A B A example you sang.

1. One way in which the two A sections are the same is that

   a. they both end on *do.*

   b. all the notes are the same except for the last note.

   c. both A sections repeat.

   d. only the second measures in both A sections are the same.

2. One way the B section is different from the A section is that

   a. only the last measure in B is different from the last measure in A.

   b. the B section has completely different rhythms.

   c. all of the notes in the B section are different from the notes in the A section.

   d. the B section is in a different key.

3. Compare the notes in the first A section with the notes in the last A section. Circle the note that is different in the last A section.

Name _____ Date _____

Ties and Slurs

1. Suppose that there are no ties or slurs in the refrain of the song "Trampin'" on page 287. Clap the rhythm.

2. Add ties where they belong in the refrain. What happens when two notes are tied together?   (Circle one)

   A. The two notes are sung together as one.
   B. The second note has a loud accent.
   C. The first note is silent.
   D. Both notes want attention.

Clap it again, but use the ties this time.

3. Add slurs where they belong in the refrain. When two notes are connected with a slur,   (Circle one)

   E. the first note is more important than the second note.
   F. the second note is shorter than the first note.
   G. the two notes are sung smoothly together.
   H. a slur is exactly the same as a tie.

Beat Bars

——— ——— ——— ———

——— ——— ——— ———

——— ——— ——— ———

——— ——— ——— ———

Pitch Ladder

RESOURCE MASTER

Curwen Hand Signs

RESOURCE MASTER

do

ti

la

so

fa

mi

re

do

Scale Stairs

TEACHER: The upper set of stairs goes from do to high do. The bottom set
of stairs goes from low so to high do.

Name _____ Date _____

Pitch Xylophone

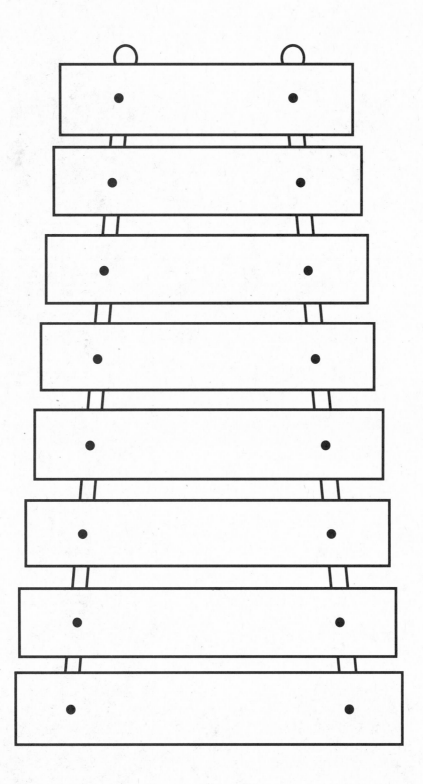

Name _____ Date _____

Scale Brackets

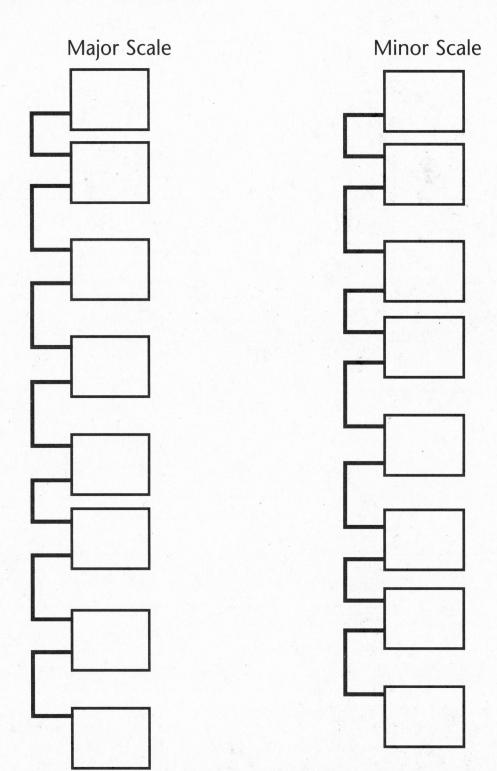

Major Scale

Minor Scale

Teacher: Give students a starting pitch and have them create a major or minor scale by writing pitch letter names in the boxes.

USE WITH GRADE 3, UNIT 1

Schoolhouse Rock Live!, Junior

Book by Scott Ferguson, Kyle Hall, and George Keating
Music and Lyrics by Lynn Ahrens, Bob Dorough, Dave Frishberg, Kathy Mandry, George Newall, Tom Yohe

Scene 1

CHILD 1: Welcome to the theatre!

CHILD 2: Let's put on a show!

CHILD 3: Which one shall we do?

CHILD 4: Let's see, wait . . . *(Pauses, shrugs shoulders.)* I don't know.

CHILD 5: We've got lessons to learn!

CHILD 6: We've got time on the clock!

CHILD 7: We're all right here at school . . .

ALL: Why not do SCHOOLHOUSE ROCK!?

(ALL improvise reactions such as "yeah," "that sounds great," "cool," etc., as a large scroll is unrolled with the words "SCHOOLHOUSE ROCK LIVE!" on it.)

CHILD 8: Remember those cartoons that you saw on TV, about grammar, life, and the great number three?

CHILD 9: Remember Interplanet Janet?

CHILD 10: I LOVED that one!

CHILD 11: And singing along with the show was such fun!

CHILD 12: But where should we start?

CHILD 13: We won't keep you guessin'!

ALL: Let's kick things off with a HISTORY lesson!

(Another scroll is unrolled, on which is written "THE PREAMBLE.")

CHILD 14: Presenting, the UNITED STATES CONSTITUTION!

Song 1: The Preamble (Company)

ALL: Hey, do you know about the U.S.A.?
Do you know about the government?
Can you tell me 'bout the Constitution?
Hey, learn about the U.S.A.!

SOLO 1: In seventeen eighty-seven, I'm told,
Our founding fathers did agree
To write a list of principles
For keepin' people free.

ALL: The U.S.A. was just starting out,
A whole brand new country.
And so our people spelled it out,
The things that we should be.

ALL: We the people
In order to form a more perfect union,
Establish justice,
Domestic tranquility,
Provide for the common defense,
Promote the general welfare,
And secure the blessings of liberty
To ourselves and our posterity,
Do ordain and establish
This constitution for the
United States of America.

For the United States of America.

End of Song

Scene 2

CHILD 15: That number was great! I learned a lot.

CHILD 16: Speaking of numbers, what else have we got?

CHILD 17: Which song was your favorite?

CHILD 18: My favorite, let's see . . . my favorite number's the one about three!

ALL: Yeah, yeah . . . let's do it!, I love that one!, *(etc.)*

(A scroll, reading "THREE IS A MAGIC NUMBER," is unrolled.)

ALL: One, two, three.

TRIO 1: Three is a magic number.
Yes, it is,
It's a magic number.

TRIO 2: Somewhere in the veil
Of ancient history,
You get three as a magic number.

TRIO 3: The past and the present and the future,

TRIO 4: Faith and hope and charity,

TRIO 5: The heart and the brain and the body
Give you three as a magic number.

ALL: A man and a woman had a little baby.
Yes, they did.
They had three in the family.
That's a magic number.

Three, six, nine, twelve, fifteen,
Eighteen, twenty-one, twenty-four,
Twenty-seven, thirty.

SOLO: Multiply backwards from three times ten:

GROUP 1: Three times ten is?

GROUP 2: Thirty!

GROUP 1: Three times nine is?

GROUP 2: Twenty-seven!

GROUP 1: Three times eight is?

GROUP 2: Twenty-four!

GROUP 1: Three times seven is?

GROUP 2: Twenty-one!

ALL: Three times six is eighteen,
Three times five is fifteen,
Three times four is twelve,
And three times three is nine,
And three times two is six.

GROUP 1: And three times one?

ALL: That's a magic number.

End of Song

Scene 3

CHILD 19: Math is great, now, don't get me wrong . . . But what about science?

CHILD 20: I've got JUST the song . . .

(A scroll is unrolled, reading "INTERPLANET JANET" across it.)

Song 3: Interplanet Janet (Company)

ALL: They say our solar system is centered around the sun.
Nine planets large and small parading by.

But somewhere out in space
There's another shining face
That you MIGHT see some night
Up in the sky waving "HI!"

Interplanet Janet, she's a galaxy girl,
A solar system Ms. from a future world.
She travels like a rocket with her comet team,
And there's never been a planet
Janet hasn't seen.

No, there's never been a planet
Janet hasn't seen.

SOLO 1: She's been to the sun, it's a lot of fun!

ALL: Hi!

DUO 1: It's a hot spot, it's a gas.

SOLO 2: Hydrogen

SOLO 3: And helium

TOGETHER: In a big, bright, glowing mass.

ALL: It's a star, it's a star,

ALL: So Janet got an autograph!

ALL: Uh, huh!

ALL: Mercury was near the sun
So Janet stopped by,
But the mercury on Mercury
Was much too high,

DUO 1: So Janet split for Venus,
But on Venus she found
She couldn't see a thing
For all the clouds around.

DUO 2: Earth looked exciting,
Kind of green and inviting,
So Janet thought she'd give it a go.

ALL: But the creatures on that planet
Looked so very weird to Janet,
She didn't even dare to say "hello."

ALL: It's a bird!
It's a plane!

ALL: Why, it must be a U.F.O.!

But it was Interplanet Janet
She's a galaxy girl,
A solar system Ms. from a future world.
She travels like a rocket with her comet team,
And there's never been a planet
Janet hasn't seen.

No, there's never been a planet
Janet hasn't seen.

SOLO 1: Mars is red,

SOLO 2: And Jupiter's big,

SOLO 3: And Saturn shows off its rings.

SOLO 1: Uranus is built on a funny tilt,

SOLO 2: And Neptune is its twin.

ALL: And Pluto, little Pluto,
Is the farthest planet from our sun.

ALL: Interplanet Janet, she's a galaxy girl,
A solar system Ms. from a future world.
She travels like a rocket with her comet team,
And there's never been a planet
Janet hasn't seen.

No, there's never been a planet
Janet hasn't seen.

End of Song

Scene 4

(The song ends and the CHILDREN begin putting their PROPS away.)

CHILD 21: Is there time for one more?

CHILD 22: If we don't dilly-dally!

CHILD 23: Here's my favorite song, for the big grand finale!

ALL: "INTERJECTIONS!" Yea!

(TWO CHILDREN go to CENTER; one coughing and sneezing, the other playing a doctor.)

Song 4: Interjections (Company)

ALL: When Reginald was home with the flu, uh-huh.
The doctor knew just what to do.

She cured the infection
With one small injection,
While Reginald uttered some interjections

(Music continues under the following dialogue.)

SOLO 1: Hey! That smarts!

SOLO 2: Ouch! That hurts!

SOLO 3: Yow! That's not fair givin' a guy a shot down there!

ALL: Interjections

SMALL GROUP: (Hey!)

ALL: Show excitement

SMALL GROUP: (Ouch!)

ALL: Or emotion.

SMALL GROUP: (Yow!)

ALL: They're generally set apart from a sentence
By an exlamation point,
Or by a comma when the feeling's not as strong.

ALL: So when you're happy,

SMALL GROUP: (Hurray!)

ALL: Or sad,

SMALL GROUP: (Aw!)

ALL: Or frightened,

SMALL GROUP: (Eek!)

ALL: Or mad,

SMALL GROUP: (Rats!)

ALL: Or excited,

SMALL GROUP: (Wow!)

ALL: Or glad,

SMALL GROUP: (Hey!)

ALL: An interjection starts a sentence right!

The game was tied at seven all, uh-huh,
When Franklin found he had the ball.
He made a connection
In the other direction,
The crowd started shoutin' out
Interjections.

(Music continues under the following dialogue.)

SOLO 1: Aw! You threw the wrong way!

SOLO 2: Darn! You just lost the game!

SOLO 3: Hooray! I'm for the other team!

ALL: Interjections

SMALL GROUP: (Aw!)

ALL: Show excitement

SMALL GROUP: (Darn!)

ALL: Or emotion.

SMALL GROUP: (H'ray!)

ALL: They're generally set apart from a sentence
By an exclamation point,
Or by a comma when the feeling's not as strong.

Interjections show excitement or emotion.
Hallelujah. Hallelujah.
Hallelujah. Yeah!

SOLO 1: Darn! That's the end!

End of Song

There Was an Old Lady

Play the musical patterns below when you see the symbol in the poem.

 Tone Chimes

(Think: Time to a - wake and greet the day!)

 Mar.

(Think: La Cu - cha - ra - cha, La Cu - cha - ra - cha)

AG

(Think: I'm bring - ing home a bab - y bum - ble bee)

SX

(Think: Au - tumn leaves are fall - ing down.)

AM

(*Think:* "Look at me skate. I'm real - ly great!")

AX

(*Think:* Here comes the bride, all dressed in white.)

BX

(*Think:* D - I - N - O - S - A - U - R)

Voice

Da da dum, da da dum, da da dum dum dum!

The Gebeta Board

Play the musical patterns below when you see the symbol in the story.

(*Think:* I am as hap-py as can be watch-ing the cat-tle graze.)

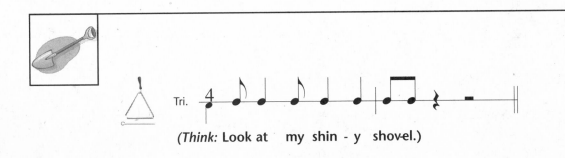

(*Think:* Look at my shin-y shov-el.)

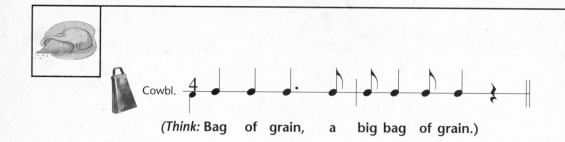

Cowbl.

(Think: Bag of grain, a big bag of grain.)

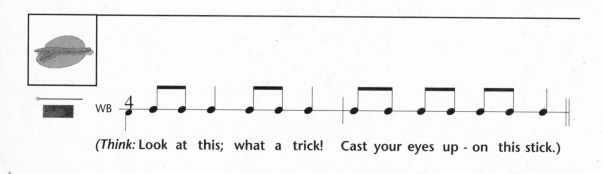

WB

(Think: Look at this; what a trick! Cast your eyes up-on this stick.)

Give Your Love Away

Words and Music by
Cristi Cary Miller

Repeat three times

Voice

AM/SM

BX

Learn to give your love a-way. It will re-turn a-noth-er day.

All the care that you can show makes the cir-cle of kind-ness grow.

Isabela and the Troll

Play the musical patterns below when you see the symbol in the story.

AM

(Think: Oh, my name is Is - a - be-la!)

BX

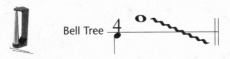

Bell Tree

Guiro

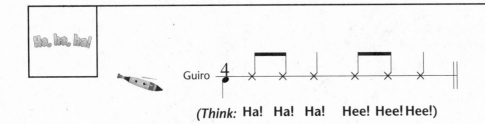

(Think: Ha! Ha! Ha! Hee! Hee! Hee!)

Cowbl.

Tamb.

WB

Voice
(Snoring sounds)

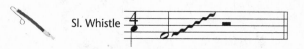
Sl. Whistle

Name _____ Date _____

Sad Sack Song

Words and Music by
Cristi Cary Miller

Name _____ Date _____

Happy Sack Song

Words and Music by
Cristi Cary Miller

Name _____ Date _____

Patriotic Words

You can write your own patriotic song! Choose the melody to one of
the songs below, or pick a favorite that is not listed here. Hum the
tune to yourself. If possible, look at the music to your song. Then write
new words. You can honor an event, a person, or even a famous site.

"Yankee Doodle"
"America"
"America, the Beautiful"
"You're a Grand Old Flag"
"This Land Is Your Land"

_____

_____

_____

_____

_____

_____

_____

Hispanic Heritage

RESOURCE MASTER (C•2)

The countries settled by Spanish-speaking people cover a huge area.
(Don't forget that the Spanish settled large areas of the United States
as well!) Here is a map with the names of those countries left blank.
Write in as many as you know. Then look at an atlas or an encyclope-
dia. Fill in the rest of the names. Make your map as colorful as those
countries are.

Name _____ Date _____

Fall Harvest Feasts

In the United States, we celebrate Thanksgiving on the fourth Thursday in November. In Canada, Thanksgiving is celebrated in October. There are other holidays in the Northern Hemisphere that celebrate the fall harvest. Some of them come as early as August!

Here is a list of some of these other harvest feasts:

- Dozynki (Poland)
- Grape Harvest (Azores)
- Oktoberfest (Germany)
- Samhain (Celtic)
- Sukkot (Jewish)

Find a recipe in a cookbook or from your family, for one of the special foods served at these harvest feasts. Your teacher may assign you a specific feast and a category of food (appetizer, main course, side dish, dessert). On a separate sheet of paper or on an index card, write down the recipe. Be careful to list the ingredients, quantities, and instructions accurately. Draw or cut out a picture of the food.

Work with your classmates to make a class recipe book. Decide together how to organize the recipes. Then design a cover, and bind the book. If possible, plan your own feast day. Each student can prepare one of the foods for everyone to enjoy!

Scary Clues

Here's a Halloween crossword puzzle for you to solve.

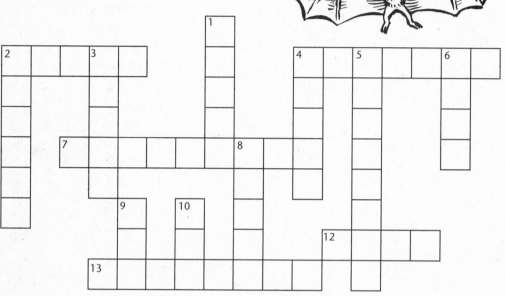

Across

2. It's not your bed, but it wears a sheet.

4. On Halloween, this can be your street clothes.

7. Where the dead are buried

12. A werewolf's "song" to the moon

13. Trick-or-treat announcer

apple	fur	mask
boo	ghost	party
candy	goblin	scare
costume	graveyard	skeleton
doorbell	howl	

Down

1. Food, dancing, and decorations

2. One of these may be "hob"

3. What a monster may do to you

4. Sweet treat

5. Bones, bones, bones!

6. Face it.

8. Bobbing prize

9. Fright night word

10. Halloween cats have black

_____.

Name _____ Date _____

Winter Festivals

Christmas, Hanukkah, and Kwanzaa all fall near the winter solstice, the darkest time of the year in our part of the world. Is it any wonder that each of these holidays is celebrated with lights—and lots of them? Families and friends, steaming hot food, colorful decorations, stories, and songs provide warmth on these winter days.

Choose a symbol of light from one of these three celebrations. Create an original design that uses the symbol. Use colored markers to get the bright tones that would be most appropriate for the celebrations.

"I Have a Dream"

We remember Dr. Martin Luther King, Jr., on the third Monday in January, which is the Monday that comes closest to his birthday. Since 1986, this day has been a national holiday. It honors the man who was probably the most important figure in the civil rights movement in our country.

Starting in the 1950s, Dr. King, a minister, was in the front lines of protests against the treatment of African Americans. Although his activities were focused in the South, the North had its ways of keeping African Americans from their full rights as well. In the summer of 1963, President Kennedy announced a new civil rights bill that would come before Congress. There was a great hurry to act because protests were breaking out across the land.

The most amazing event of that summer was the March on Washington. On August 28, about 200,000 people gathered in front of the Lincoln Memorial. The highlight of that day was Dr. King's speech. He started out reading a prepared speech. Before long, he put the speech aside. He drew on a phrase he had once used: "I have a dream." That dream was of equal rights for all people, an end to hatred, and a joining of hands.

How would you have advertised the March on Washington in your hometown? Make a poster that captures its spirit and purpose. Sketch your ideas on paper, and then create a powerful, full-sized presentation.

Name _____ Date _____

Chinese New Year

The Chinese calendar is based on the moon. As a result, its 15-day new year's celebration can start anytime from January 21 to February 19. It depends on when the new moon appears. The celebration then ends at the full moon.

The holiday is celebrated with special foods, parades, and gift giving. Family gatherings are important, and ancestors are honored. Houses become brightened with displays of poems written on red paper, plants and flowers, and fruits. Each day has special rituals. It is a time of hope and prayer for a good year.

The Chinese languages are written in characters, each with its own meaning. Here are a few.

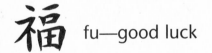 福 fu—good luck   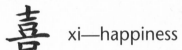 喜 xi—happiness

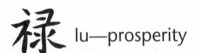 禄 lu—prosperity   财 cai—wealth

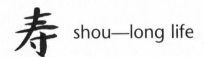 寿 shou—long life   和 he—harmony

Make a Chinese New Year card. Take a sheet of red paper. Fold it in half. Decorate the front and the inside with Chinese characters, calendar-animal symbols, or other things that have to do with Chinese culture. Show your card to your classmates.

An Irish Tale

St. Patrick is the patron saint of Ireland. He was born around the year 385 in Wales and grew up to become bishop of Ireland. He died on March 17 in the year 461. Ever since, he has been remembered on that day.

There is a lot of interesting folklore about St. Patrick. None of it has been proved true. Nevertheless, the holiday has become very popular. On St. Patrick's Day, people wear green—the color of Ireland. The three-leaf green shamrock is also commonly seen at St. Patrick's Day festivities. Parades in large cities like Chicago, Boston, and New York draw huge crowds. Irish music fills many restaurants, which also serve traditional Irish foods. It is a fun day!

Here is one verse to a song about St. Patrick's Day. Write your own chorus that is four lines long. Then sing your song to any tune you know, or make up your own melody.

As I was walking down the street
One fine St. Patrick's day, I met a lad all
dressed in green, And he had this to say:

_____

_____

_____

_____

Celebrate the Earth

Spring is when Earth blooms with new life. To celebrate spring and to remind people to take care of our planet, April 22 is set aside each year as Earth Day.

Use the clues to solve the acrostic puzzle below. Then write the letters in circles on the spaces at the bottom of the page. The first one is done for you. Unscramble these letters to get an Earth Day message.

A bicycle is an Earth-friendly (V) E (H) I C L E .

These grow in forests. (O) ___ ___ ___ ___

You collect cans to ___ ___ ___ ___ ___ ___ (O) .

Some return north in spring. ___ ___ (O) ___ ___

This makes up a lawn. ___ ___ (O) ___ ___

This makes life on Earth possible (and warm). (O) ___ ___

___ ___ (O) (O) ___ plants make their own food.

We must try not to pollute the (O) ___ ___ we breathe.

In spring, there is less (O) ___ ___ (O) than in summer.

Place circled letters here:

V H ___ ___ ___ ___ ___ ___ ___ ___ ___ ___ ___ ___

Unscrambled:

___ ___ ___ ___ ___ ___ ___ ___ ___ ___ ___ ___ ___

Cinco de Mayo

If Mexico won its freedom from Spain, then why does it celebrate a victory over France? In 1862, a free Mexico was about 50 years old. It owed other countries a great deal of money. Although Mexico worked this trouble out with several governments, France and Mexico could not reach an agreement. The French emperor sent troops to Mexico. A small army of Mexicans defeated the French at the Battle of Puebla on May 5. Mexicans and Mexican Americans celebrate this amazing victory each year with dancing, parades, food, and colorful costumes.

Cut out the costumes below. Make cardboard figures of a boy and a girl to fit into them. Color the costumes, and get ready to join the Cinco de Mayo celebration!

Listening Map Instructions

LM-3 Guadalquivir

Use with Unit 1, Lesson 7

Distribute a copy of the listening map to each student. Introduce the Andean instruments to them as drawn in the map. Start by clapping and saying the rhythm pattern at the top of the map. As they listen to the song, see if they can recognize this pattern when it occurs in the music. It is played throughout the song on different instruments: the Quena (wooden flute), Bombo (hand drum—animal skin on top with fur, played with a whittled stick; head of mallet is covered with leather), and Charango (ukelele-like instrument—the back of this instrument is made from the shell of an armadillo). In each frame, these instruments are shown in the pattern of the ♩ ♩ ♫ ♩ rhythm. Students should be able to tap the instruments they are listening to in this rhythmic pattern. The dancers represent the portions of the music that are more flowing and dancelike at :58 and 1:51.

LM-4 Pata Pata

Use with Unit 1, Lesson 8

Distribute a copy of the listening map to each student. Following the Introduction, this lively song features a woman singing using syncopation. As the students listen to "Pata Pata" they will feel a strong sense of rhythm and beat. In the first section, have students clap the beat, listening for the two eighth notes on beat 3. Once they can identify those two notes, they can insert two taps for count 3, while continuing to clap the beat on counts 1, 2, and 4. As they listen to the second section, how does the music change? (It becomes smoother and winds up and down—like a snake). In this section, the eighth note pattern is shown on the back of the snake in two measure sections. Have students tap the dots on the snake to find this pattern. In the third section, beat four has the even eighth note pattern. Tap on the single dancers for the quarter notes and the pair of dancers for the eighth notes. The last section represents the layering effect of the music.

LM-6 A Clock at Night

Use with Unit 2, Lesson 6

Distribute a copy of the listening map to each student. Discuss how music can make you move your body to the rhythm and sound of the instruments. Sometimes the tempo can change, causing you to change the way you are moving. Listen to the song and have students move like the tick tock of a clock in the A section—side to side. They can do this with their heads as they are seated or with their bodies if standing. In the B section, the music becomes heavy and more legato. Have them experiment moving their arms in circles, a more flowing movement. When the A section returns, movement becomes more defined and directional.

Listening Map Instructions

LM-8 Les saluts

Use with Unit 3, Lesson 2

Distribute a copy of the listening map to each student. Have students watch the map as they listen to the music. Ask them to feel the beat and count the number of beats in each phrase (Section A has two 16-beat phrases and section B has two 8-beat phrases. They will hear a fermata, or hold, in the middle of the 8-beat phrase). Have students study the map to learn the dance, and then try the dance using one or two circles, depending on the size of the room. Section A—circle clockwise holding hands for the first 16 beats; circle counter clockwise for the next 16 beats. Section B—hold hands and move to center for 4 counts, back out for 4 counts, back in for 4 counts and stop with hands in the air (fermata) and back out for the last 4 counts. Section A—same as before.

LM-11 Trio for Piano, Violin, and Cello No. 39, Finale ("Gypsy Rondo")

Use with Unit 4, Lesson 8

Distribute a copy of the listening map to each student. Explain rondo form (ABACA Coda). The "Gypsy Rondo" is an example of rondo form with a variety of smaller sections within each larger section. Because of the complexity of this particular piece, it may be helpful to pause the CD at the end of each section. As students listen to the music, have them follow the caravan of gypsies travelling across the country. The A section shows the female gypsies happily dancing near their wagon.

The B section shows the gypsy children skipping and stomping to the music. The C section shows the gypsy men dancing near the fire as the music changes into a minor mode. (Representing ABACA). In the Coda, the caravan of gypsies is moving away.

LM-13 Gigue from Suite No. 1 for Cello by J. S. Bach

Use with Unit 5, Lesson 4

The Gigue is in AB form, with both sections repeated. Ask students to tap each beat bar on the map as they listen to the A section, noting the contrast between legato (represented by the squiggles) and staccato, or detached, articulation. Explain that the cellist creates the smooth, legato sound by playing several notes in one bow. For a more detached, staccato sound, the cellist changes bow and accents the beginning of each note slightly by applying pressure to the bow. Ask students to listen to the B section and raise their hands whenever they hear a change from smooth, legato sounds to shorter, detached (staccato) sounds. The music moves quickly, so they will need to stay alert!

LM-14 La raspa

Use with Unit 6, Lesson 2

Distribute a copy of the listening map to each student. Listen to the music and have the students patsch (pat laps) to the steady beat in section A (represented by the trumpet). Then have them play the rhythm of the melody on their laps.

Listening Map Instructions

Study the map to discover how students will show the beat with three sounds on it. (Clap beats 1, 2, 3 in the first example measure, and patsch the rhythm on beats 1, 2, and 3 of the second measure. Rest on beat 4 in both example measures.) Divide the class into two groups. One group will clap the steady beat while the other patsches the rhythm of the melody. Listen to section B and create a dance to the music. If you choose, students could do the Mexican Hat Dance in subsequent listenings.

LM-19 Brafferton Village/Walsh's Hornpipe (Irish folk music)

Use with Spotlight on Celebrations

Distribute a copy of the listening map to each student. This piece follows a traditional pattern for traditional Irish music. There is a short introduction that is similar to the A section, followed by two A sections and two B sections. Point out the instruments in the center of the listening map. The bodhran is a round, open-backed drum that is played with the drum head vertical. The drummer holds the drum on the knee and plays it with a two-headed beater. The accordion is not like the one students may be familiar with that has a piano-like keyboard on one side. The accordion heard on this recording is a button accordion, which has rows of buttons on both sides. The buttons on the right are for the melody and the buttons on the right are for the chords. The Northumbrian pipes (also known as Ulleann pipes) are not as loud as traditional Scottish bagpipes. The piper squeezes a bellows under the arm to fill the pipes with air (unlike the Scottish pipes where the player blows into a pipe.

Guadalquivir

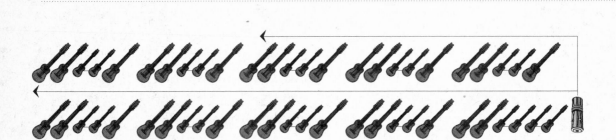

Quena   **Bombo**   **Yelp**

Charango

Pata Pata

Introduction 4 measures

A Clock at Night

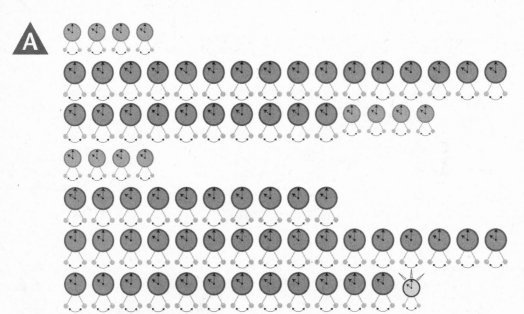

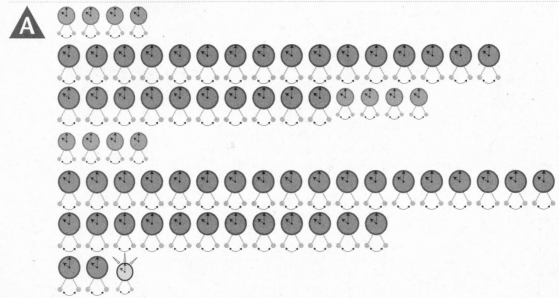

Les saluts

Introduction

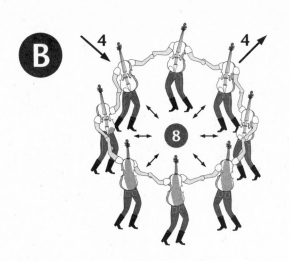

Form played six times total

Trio for Piano, Violin, and Cello No. 39, Finale ("Gypsy Rondo")

Gigue
from Suite No. 1 for Cello

A

tr〰

B

Name _____ Date _____

La raspa
(Mexican folk dance)

Name _____ Date _____

Brafferton Village/
Walsh's Hornpipe
(Irish folk music)

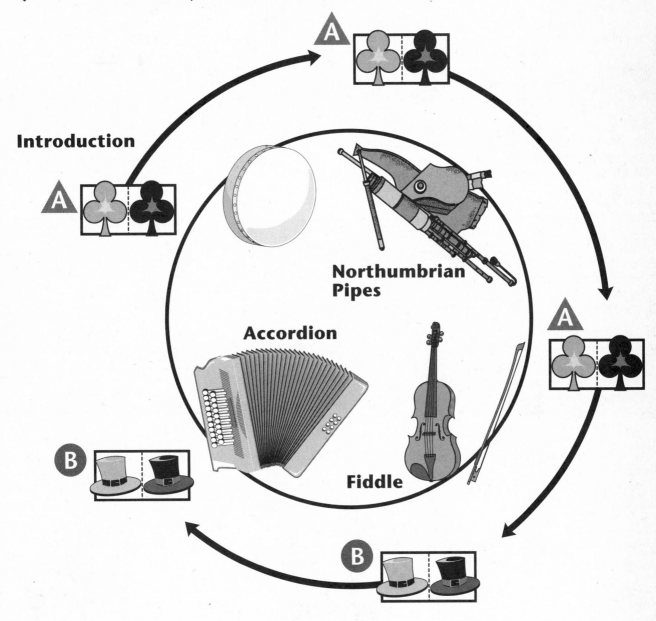

Introduction

A

A

Northumbrian Pipes

Accordion

A

Fiddle

B

B

Introduction to Signed Songs

by The Reverend Dr. Peggy A. Johnson, pastor
Christ United Methodist Church of the Deaf

The use of sign language along with vocal music has become a popular way of adding interest and expression to a song. Frequently a student who struggles with vocal music will find a successful outlet for expression through the use of sign language. Sign language has been used as an educational tool for reading comprehension and language development. Typically it appears as a picture for every spoken or written English word. This is known as "Signed English." It follows the grammar of English.

American Sign Language (ASL) is different from Signed English. It uses signs for words or concepts, but the grammar is produced with the eyes and face and through the movements of the body. It does not follow the word order of spoken English for the most part and has its own structure. ASL is the native language of people who describe themselves as Culturally Deaf. Deaf Culture is a community of people consisting of deaf and hard-of-hearing people who:

• use ASL,

• have primary personal relationships with people who also use this language,

• have typically attended state residential schools for the deaf where ASL is the mode of communication and instruction, and

• have unique history, traditions, and advocacy organizations.

For people in the Deaf Culture, ASL is used in their music and poetry, not Signed English.

It is difficult for a hearing person to sing an English word-order song and to sign in ASL at the same time. Most of the sign language section of this book is done in English word-order for that reason. However, some ASL grammar is incorporated for the purpose of linguistical awareness, and ASL grammar often creates a more artistic rendering of the movements. A phrase such as "lift up your eyes" in English would be best translated into ASL as "your eyes, lift up." The latter is more effective in a signed song because ending on a sign such as "lift up" has a better flow.

Hearing people who are fascinated by and attracted to signed music might consider taking a course on ASL. It would help increase one's skill in the language. People who study "foreign" languages often develop a sensitivity for the culture and people from which the language sprang. It is a sign of respect for the culture of the people for whom this language is their native language.

A good music program provides many benefits to students and teachers. Multicultural awareness is increased when we sing songs in Spanish or German or Japanese. By "singing" in ASL, students can gain multicultural awareness of the Deaf Culture.

Rules for Signed Singing

1) Every word does not need to be signed. Keep the signs flowing one to the other, and be sensitive to the length of the word in the music. The sign for a whole-note word should be stretched out longer and slower than a quarter-note word.

2) Right-handed and left-handed people sign opposite because there is a dominant, active hand and a passive hand in many signs. For a performance, it is best to have everyone signing one way or the other, either everyone do it right-handed or everyone do it left-handed.

3) When teaching a song, it is ideal to teach it with your back to the students facing a large mirror. In that way the directionality is correct. When a teacher faces a group of students and signs, the students tend to mirror the teacher, and then the sign goes in the opposite direction.

4) A person's face needs to be appropriate to the mood of the word being sung. "Sad" should look sad, "joyful" should look joyful, etc.

5) If at all possible, invite a native signer to assist with the teaching of the song. This shows respect for the Deaf Culture, and a live example of a sign is always preferable to a drawn picture of a sign in a book.

Perfection is not the goal. The joy of music expressed in sign language can occur even when the signs are not performed perfectly.

Alphabet and Numbers

SIGNING MASTER

MANUAL ALPHABET AND NUMBERS 1–10

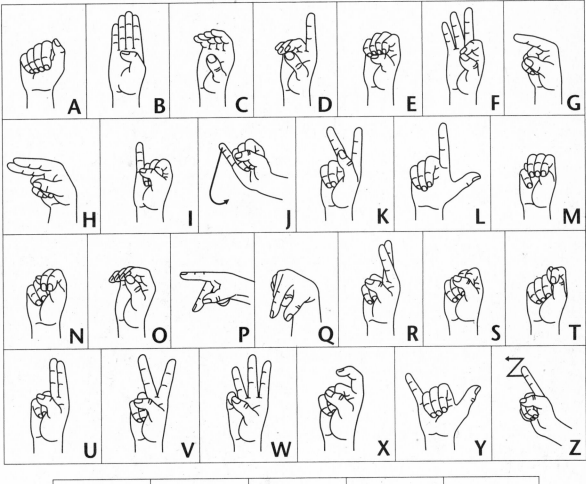

Yellow Submarine (Refrain)

1. We

The right index finger touches the right shoulder (pointing downward) and draws it across the body to the left shoulder.

2. Live

Both hands are in a letter "L" hand shape and begin at the waist in front of the body. Both hands draw up toward the shoulders.

3. Yellow

The right hand makes a "Y" hand shape and shakes it to the right side of the body.

4. Submarine

The left hand is in a flat hand position with palm facing down in front of the body. The right hand is in the shape of a number "3" that is laying sideways. The right hand makes several forward motions under the left hand.

This Is America (page 1)

1. This

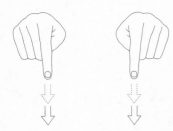

Both hands are in a number "1" hand shape in front of the body with the finger pointing downward two times.

2. America

Both hands are in front of the body with fingers interlocked and fanning outward. The interlocked hands make a full circle in front of the body.

3. Land

The right hand crosses the body and makes circular motions at the elbow of the left arm.

4. Courage

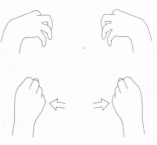

Both hands begin with a claw shape at the top of the chest. The arms draw outward and the hands tighten into a fist.

5. Faith

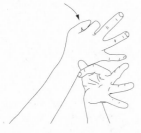

Both hands are in a letter "F" hand shape. The right hand taps the top of the left hand.

6. Honor

Both hands are in the shape of a letter "H" in front of the body. The right hand is slightly higher than the left. Both hands begin above the head and make a downward curving motion.

This Is America (page 2)

SIGNING MASTER S•3

7. True

The index finger of the right hand begins at the mouth and extends outward.

8. Equality

Both hands are in the right angle hand shape in front of the body with hands facing each other. The fingertips tap each other.

9. Hope

The left arm with hand in a right angle position is held to the left side of body, slightly elevated. The right arm faces the left arm with a right angle hand position. The hands "wave" at each other.

10. Pride

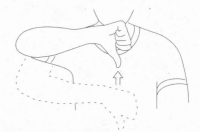

The right hand in a number "10" hand shape draws a vertical line from the waist to the top of the chest with the thumb.

11. Unity

Both hands link together in front of the body with the thumb and middle fingers connected.

12. Liberty

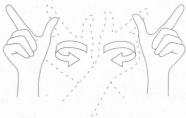

Both hands are in a letter "L" hand shape. Hands are crossed in front of the body and then breaking in opposite directions with arms extending outward.

Name _____ Date _____

Eight Days of Hanukkah (page 1)

1. Eight

The right hand thumb and the middle fingertips touch each other. The other fingers on the hand point upward.

2. Days

The left arm lays across the waist with palm down. The right arm (with a hand shape of a number "1" places its elbow on the left hand. Then the right arms makes a 45 degree sweep of the arm from an upward position to its resting place on top of the left arm.

3. Hanukkah

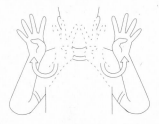

Both hands are in the number "4" hand shape in front of the face with palms facing inward. The hands move outward to opposite sides of the body.

4. Happy

Make upward sweeps from the waist to the shoulders with both hands in a flat hand position with palms toward the body. The face should have a smiling expression.

5. Nights

The left hand is positioned sideways in front of the waist with the palm downward. The right hand is placed on the left hand with the palm facing downward and the right-angle hand shape.

6. Pleasure (enjoy)

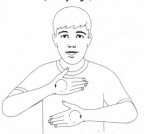

Both hands are flat and facing the body. The right hand is higher than the left hand. Both hands make circular motions in front of the body.

Eight Days of Hanukkah (page 2)

7. Festival

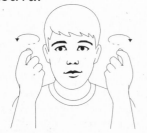

Both hands are in a letter "X" hand shape on either side of the body. Both hands make small circular motions as if waving a flag.

8. Light

Both hands are together in a closed position in front of the body. The fingers of both hands fan outward and upward and end up on either side of the body.

9. Gifts

Both hands are in a letter "X" hand shape in front of the body. Both hands make one forward motion away from the body as if giving something.

10. Memories

Both hands are in a letter "A" hand shape. The right hand thumb touches the forehead and then moves down to the left hand with is in front of the body. The right thumb touches the left thumb.

11. Bring (Raise)

Both hands are in a flat hand position in front of the body with palms facing upward. Both hands begin at the left side of the body and sweep across the body to the right side maintaining the palms-up position.

12. Wonderful

Both hands have open palms facing outward with the fingers together. Beginning with the left side of the body the hands sweep across to the right side in a parallel motion.

Name _____ Date _____

Eight Days of Hanukkah (page 3)

13. Let's

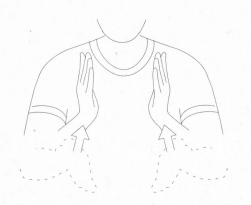

Both hands are at the sides with palms facing inward. They both point the fingertip side of the hand in and upward direction with two quick motions.

14. Count

The left hand is in a flat hand position in the front of the body with the palm facing upward. The right hand is in the hand shape of a letter "F" with palm facing downward. The right hand draws quick outward motions on the left palm.

15. Ways

The right and left hands held out to either side of the body with palms facing inward. The hands then move forward forming a path in front of the body.

Shalom Chaveyrim
(Shalom, My Friends)

1. Peace (Shalom)

Both hands are together with flat palms facing. The wrists turn the palms and then the palms separate to each side of the body with the palms facing downward.

2. My

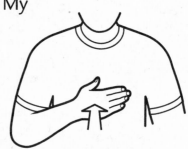

The right hand in a "5" hand shape comes toward the body and rests on the chest.

3. Friend

Both hands in an "X" shape with forefingers linking once with the right hand on top and then a second linking motion with the left hand on top.

4. We

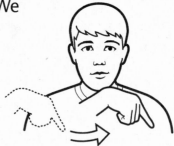

The right index finger touches the right shoulder (pointing downward) and draws it across the body to the left shoulder.

5. Meet

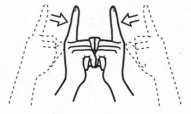

Both hands are in the number "1" hand shape and begin on either side of the body. The hands come together in front of the body and knuckles touch.

6. Again

The left hand is in a flat hand position with the palm facing upward. The right hand makes a right angle position and dives downward into the center of the left palm.

Name _____ Date _____

Consider Yourself (page 1)

1. Consider

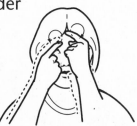

Both hands are in a number "1" hand shape at the front temple of the head. Both forefingers make small circles in front of the temple.

2. Yourself

The right hand is in a number "10" hand shape. It extends out away from the body with two quick shakes.

3. Home

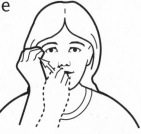

The right hand assumes a right angle hand shape and first touches the lips and then brings that hand across the right side of the face and lands on the check.

4. Family

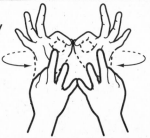

Both hands are in a letter "F" hand shape in front of the body touching thumb and forefinger. Then both hands separate and make a semicircle to the side and end up in front of the body with the little finger of each hand touching.

5. We

The right index finger touches the right shoulder (pointing downward) and draws it across the body to the left shoulder.

6. Like (taken to you)

The right hand begins at the chest with palm turned inward. The thumb and middle finger make a motion as if to be pulling a thread off the body. The hand is drawn out away from the body with the thumb and middle finger coming together.

Consider Yourself (page 2)

SIGNING MASTER S•6

7. Strong

Both hands are in a fist shape to the left side of the body. The first are drawn across the body to the right side.

8. Clear

Both hands are together in a closed position in front of the body. The fingers of both hands fan outward and upward and end up on either side of the body.

9. Get along

Both hands are in front of the body in a letter "A" hand shape with knuckles touching. The hands shake up and down two times.

10. Accept (Well In)

Both hands begin with palms down out in front of the body with a slight curve of the hand. Then the hands are drawn in toward the body assuming a right angle hand shape and resting at the chest.

11. Furniture

The right hand in the letter "F" hand shape is held up in front of the body with palm facing outward. The hand is waved back and forth in a small motion to the right side of the body.

12. Not

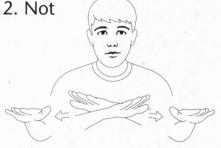

Both hands are crossed in front of the body with palms facing downward. Then the hands cross in front of the body and arms end up extended on both sides.

USE WITH GRADE 3, SIGNING

Consider Yourself (page 3)

---

13. A lot

Hands facing each other with fingers curved. Hands move outward.

14. Spare

The left hand is in a letter "A" hand shape. The right hand is in a letter "V" hand shape. The right hand grips the left hand placing the letter "V" on the back of the left hand.

15. Who cares?

The right hand is in a number "1" hand shape in front of the body. The index finger touches the nose and then pulls away and points outward.

16. Whatever

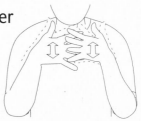

Both hands are in a number "5" hand shape in front of the body with palms facing toward the body with thumbs on top. Both hands move back and forth from the body with the fingers passing through each other.

17. Have

Both hands touch the chest with a right angle hand shape.

18. Share

The left hand is in front of the body with the palm facing inward. The right hand makes back-and-forth motions on the left hand between the left thumb and the index finger with the side of the right hand.

Consider Yourself (page 4)

19. Friend (Mate)

Both hands in an "X" shape with forefingers linking once with the right hand on top and then a second linking motion with the left hand on top.

20. Don't Want (Don't want to have)

Both hands are in a claw position in front of the body with palms facing inward. Then both hands turn palms downward and outward in one quick thrust away from the body.

21. Fuss

Right hand in a claw-shaped position. Fingertips touch the chest.

22. After

Both hands are in front of the body in a flat hand position with palms facing inward. The right hand is on the outside and it proceeds outward from the body. The left hand remains stationary.

23. Say (State)

The index finger of the right hand starts at the mouth and goes outward.

24. One (of us)

Both hands link together in front of the body with the thumb and middle fingers connected.

Name _____ Date _____

Evergreen, Everblue (page 1)

1. Always

The right hand is in a number "1" hand shape pointing upward. The index finger makes continuous small circles to the right side of the body.

2. Green

The right hand makes a "G" hand shape and shakes it on the right side of the body.

3. Blue

The right hand makes a "B" hand shape and shakes it on the right side of the body.

4. Same

Both hands make a "Y" hand shape out in front with palms facing down. The hands move parallel across the body from left to right.

5. Beginning

The right hand is in a number "1" hand shape. The left hand is in a number "5" hand shape with the palm facing the middle of the body. The right index finger is inserted between the index and middle finger and is twisted so that the right palm begins downward and twists upward.

6. Now

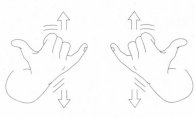

Both hands are in a letter "Y" hand shape with palms facing upward in front of the body. The hands make an up and down bouncing motion.

Evergreen, Everblue (page 2)

SIGNING MASTER S•7

7. Time

The right index finger taps the left wrist.

8. Depends (it's up to)

Both hands are in a number "1" hand shape in front of the body with palms facing downward. The index fingers of both hands make a right angle. The hands held in this position bounce up and down a few times.

9. Me

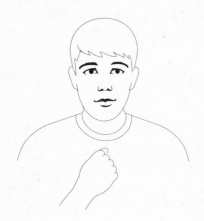

The right index finger points to the middle of the chest.

10. You (Plural)

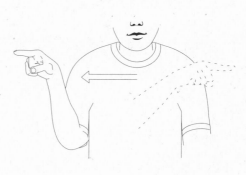

The index finger of the right hand starts at the left and sweeps across the body to the right.

Grade 3 Answer Key

Resource Master 5-7
The Conductor's Job

1. Conductors use a baton.

2. Conductors choose music, teach musicians, and rehearse.

3. Conductors often attend conservatories.

4. Bernstein wanted children to learn about classical music.

Resource Master 5-8
Mid-Unit Review

1. a. 2   d. 1

    b. 1   e. 3

    c. 4   f. 1

2. a. 3   b. 4   c. 3

5. It begins on an upbeat.

Resource Master 5-10
The Shepherd and His Sheep

A shepherd in the Scottish Highlands played his bagpipes for his lambs. The lambs laughed, giggled, and gabbed because they were glad to hear the bagpipe music. One day, the shepherd's bagpipes broke. The lambs sobbed and groaned. The shepherd travelled to the city and bought new bagpipes.

Resource Master 5-11
Around and Around

1. They symbolize community unity.

2. The gavotte was first performed in France.

3. In Korea, at the Harvest Moon Festival in the fall, people perform the kanggangsuwollae dance.

4. The dancers clap each other's hands and sing songs.

Resource Master 6-5
Getting Centered

1.

Uno de enero
(The First of January)

Mexican Folk Song

2. Students' ostinatos will vary.

Resource Master 6-6
Dancing with Props

1. The movements represent things in nature, such as flowers, butterflies, and rivers.

2. Middle-aged men perform the Baris dance.

3. They wear scarves, beads, and flowers.

Grade 3 Answer Key

Resouce Master 6-7
Pitches and Centers

3.

a.
do do do so, la, la, so, mi mi re re do

b.
mi re do re mi mi mi mi re re mi re do

c.
do la re la ti do la re re la

d.
do re mi so so la so mi do re mi mi re do re

Resource Master 6-8
Mid-Unit Review

1. F—Melodies usually begin and end on the tonal center.

2. T

3. F—The Chiapas region is in the south of Mexico.

5. F—"One More River" tells the story of Noah and his ark.

6.

7.

Resource Master 6-9
Speed It Up

1. Most students will insert a slash between the fourth and fifth sentences, as Sandra begins pedaling faster and faster.

2. Students' paragraphs will vary. Check that they include building action.

Resource Master C-2
Hispanic Heritage

Resource Master C-4
Scary Clues

Resource Master C-9
Celebrate the Earth

TREES	SUNGREEN
RECYCLE	AIR
BIRDS	HEAT
GRASS	
SAVE THE EARTH